PC-3052

MATHEMATICS DEPARTMENT
ALVERNO COLLEGE
MILWAUKEE, WI 53234-3922

W9-BWS-931

Exploring
with
Squares
and
Cubes

□ □ □ □ □ □ □ □ □ □

Grades 4–9

Ron Kremer

DALE SEYMOUR PUBLICATIONS

Cover design: Rachel Gage
Labsheet art and other cartoons: Ron Kremer
Editor: Holly Wunder

Order number DS01906
ISBN 0-86651-470-8

**DALE
SEYMOUR
PUBLICATIONS**
P.O. BOX 10888
PALO ALTO, CA 94303

4 5 6 7 8 9 10 11 12-MA-95 94 93 92

In memory of Robert Wirtz, whose teaching style demonstrated the importance of being playful with numbers.

Contents

Preface   vii
How to Use this Book   ix
A Little Education Theory   xi
Setting the Stage   xii

□ **Arrangements of Four Squares**
1. Exploring Arrangements of Four Squares   1
2. Sorting Arrangements of Four Squares   4

□ **Arrangements of Five Squares**
3. Exploring Arrangements of Five Squares   7
4. Exploring Pentominoes   11
5. Making Pentomino Puzzles   20
6. Evaluating Irregular Pentomino Puzzles   23
7. Evaluating Regular Pentomino Puzzles   31
8. Designing Pentomino Puzzles (I)   35
9. Designing Pentomino Puzzles (II)   38
10. Sequencing Pentominoes   42
11. "Packing" or Tiling Pentominoes (an optional art application)   46

□ **Arrangements of Six Squares**
12. Exploring Arrangements of Six Squares   49
13. Exploring Hexominoes   54
14. Designing and Evaluating Hexomino Puzzles (I)   59
15. Designing and Evaluating Hexomino Puzzles (II)   66
16. "Hexiosaurs" (an optional science application)   70
17. Sorting Hexominoes by Perimeter   74
18. Grouping Hexominoes by Embedded Components   77
19. Exploring Hexomic Roots   82
20. Exploring Multiple Roots of Hexominoes   84
21. Sequencing Hexominoes   89
22. Folding Hexominoes into Cubes   92

□ **Arrangements of Four Cubes**
23. Exploring Arrangements of Four Cubes   97
24. Exploring Surface Area   103

☐ **Arrangements of Five Cubes**

25. Exploring Irregular Arrangements of Five Cubes   107
26. Constructing 4 x 4 x 4 Cubes   110
27. Constructing 3 x 3 x 3 Cubes   117
28. Constructing Prisms with Irregular Arrangements of Five Cubes   121
29. Designing Prisms Made of Irregular Arrangements of Five Cubes   125
30. Constructing Symmetrical Solids with Irregular Arrangements
     of Five Cubes   130
31. Sorting Irregular Arrangements of Five Cubes   135
32. Exploring Multiple Roots of Irregular Arrangements of Five Cubes   136
33. Sequencing Irregular Arrangements of Five Cubes   143

Grid Paper Patterns   147

Arithmetic is a necessary and important part of mathematics, just as spelling and grammar are necessary parts of creative writing. Arithmetic is not, however, the end of the mathematics curriculum. Children need to be drawn out of the safety of the algorithm and memorized tables into the open-ended, playful risk of exploratory mathematics.

If a risk exists for students, it also exists for you the teacher. Be bold enough to dive into an area of mathematics that you may not be familiar with. Don't be afraid to ask questions you don't know the answers to . . . find the answers along with your students.

Over the years I have explored many of the problems in this book with students in my classes. Sometimes I've asked questions without even knowing whether those questions had answers at all . . . and students *have* found answers! One year I was delighted to learn from one of my students that there are twenty-eight irregular arrangements of five cubes, not twenty-seven as I had believed for years. He showed me that it is impossible to turn the arrangement (1) below in any way so that it looks like (2). I had overlooked the mirror image:

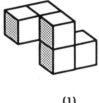   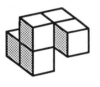

(1)   (2)

There are two problems in this book for which I have not provided solutions: finding a linear sequence of all thirty-five hexominoes and finding a linear sequence of all twenty-eight irregular arrangements of five cubes. One of your students will probably find a solution for each one.

Remember that exploratory activities take time. Some of the explorations in this book work best when students can work on them for a short time every day over a period of several days. This allows the "percolation" time students need to discover new patterns and relationships in the data they are collecting.

Relax and have fun!

Ron Kremer

How to Use this Book

Exploring with Squares and Cubes is a series of 33 explorations. In each one, students experiment with different arrangements of squares or cubes to gain new insights into geometry.

Teacher Notes

The *Teacher Notes* for each exploration suggest ways to get students started. *Be sure to keep the process student-centered.* Your role as a teacher is to create a playful, positive environment that encourages students to think creatively about an open-ended problem.

Labsheets

Many of the explorations in this book include *labsheets.* You can duplicate these and distribute them to students—who, in turn, can work on the problems by themselves. Of course, you can conduct the explorations with or without the labsheets. For example, you might just use the questions on a labsheet to motivate students and introduce them to the problem they're about to explore.

Independent Exploration

While all students benefit from responsive interaction with the teacher, some may be able to work more independently. The "Independent Exploration" sections in the Teacher Notes provide ideas for how students can use the labsheets on their own.

If you have students follow the labsheets, you may want them to work in pairs or small groups. That way they'll still have an opportunity to collaborate, compare results, and evaluate each other's solutions.

Follow-up Discussion

All students, whether they have participated in a class discussion or worked independently with the labsheets, will benefit from the activities described in the "Follow-up" section of each exploration.

Posting solutions, evaluating solutions, and identifying patterns in them is an important part of the entire process. You may want to create a "Squares and Cubes" bulletin board in your classroom that is the focus of activity as students work to find solutions to the various problems.

Materials

The materials needed for each exploration are described in the Teacher Notes. *Be sure to save your materials so that you can use them again.* In some of the explorations, students work with pentomino and hexomino shapes. Reproducible patterns for these are provided in *Exploring with Squares and Cubes,* as well as special grid paper patterns. In later explorations, students work with irregular arrangements of three and four cubes to form the Soma puzzle cube. They may use wooden or plastic blocks—or sugar cubes—to do so. Soma puzzle cubes are also available commercially, as are plastic pentominoes, color tiles, and multilink cubes.

Robert Wirtz combined the approaches of Jean Piaget and Jerome Bruner to develop this grid. It describes many types of instructional situations.

Too often classroom instruction is conducted on the simplest level of thinking (recall) and at the highest degree of abstraction (symbolic). See the box on the grid.

The circle on the grid indicates the emphasis of this book.

It is important for students to approach a new concept at the level of *least* abstraction. They'll learn the most by *manipulating* real objects.

Students need the freedom of time and opportunity to discover concepts on their own.

The best way for students to learn mathematics is to behave like mathematicians.

That is the fundamental goal of this book.

Robert Wirtz, a leading educator in the field of mathematics, developed his approach to classroom instruction based on the combined ideas of Jerome Bruner and Jean Piaget. He used their two approaches to develop the grid on the facing page.

Piaget and Bruner

Jean Piaget described levels or stages of abstraction that children progress through as they mature. At the simplest level, the *manipulative,* children learn about the world by picking up and manipulating real objects (for example, a wooden cube). At the *representational* level, they recognize familiar objects in pictures (a drawing of a cube). At the highest level, the *abstract,* children learn to interpret symbols for an object—such as words that describe it ("a three-inch cube.")

Jerome Bruner discussed different levels of thinking. The first level involves simple recall—or *remembered experiences.* Next, *problem solving* involves discovering answers to problems posed externally by others. At the level of *independent investigation,* students seek solutions to problems they themselves have devised.

Exploring with Squares and Cubes

The intent of this book is for students to start solving problems at the manipulative level. The hope is that once students get caught up in the problems posed *externally* by the teacher, their curiosities will be engaged and they'll start to ask questions that begin with "What if . . . ?"

When this happens, students have reached the level of independent investigation—in which problems arise *internally.*

A Special Teaching Approach

Be sure not to overexplain a topic or provide answers when students seem to hesitate. That kind of teaching robs students of the learning moment, dampens curiosity, and prevents them from moving toward the level of independent investigation.

Don't hurry. *Allow students enough time to thoroughly investigate each exploration.*

Credits

One of the original explorers in the field of playing with area (pentominoes and hexominoes among other polyominoes) was Solomon Golomb. The checkerboard proof presented in Exploration 14 and referred to in Exploration 15 is based on his work: Solomon W. Golomb, *Polyominoes* (New York: Scribner, 1965), pp. 28–29.

The Soma puzzle introduced in Exploration 23 was invented by Pat Heim, a Dutch physicist. Students will rediscover the seven irregular arrangements that form the Soma puzzle cube through the same process used by the inventor.

Carry out the following large group activity before having students begin work on the explorations in this book. This activity will help students start to think about the behaviors that they use in solving problems, whether in mathematics or science.

Materials: About sixty 4" x 18" strips of manila paper

Make the following statements to students, or write the statements on the chalkboard:

- *Mathematics is a branch of science.*
- *A mathematician is a scientist.*

Then ask:

> *What are some verbs that describe the behaviors of a scientist?*

Distribute several of the manila strips to each student and have them write one verb on each strip. Encourage students to use a dark crayon and to print with large letters.

Begin selecting completed strips and posting them on the bulletin board to create a list of scientific behaviors. If the list seems short, draw out more responses by discussing the words already posted. It may help to have students think about the different kinds of scientists: astronomers, biologists, oceanographers, and so on.

Example list:

record	explore	collect
study	think	experiment
list	analyze	test
examine	hypothesize	observe
sort	collect	organize
compare	display	evaluate
measure	identify	classify
extrapolate	rank	compute
describe	predict	calculate

Then ask students which verbs in the list describe what they have been doing just now. (Example responses: collecting, posting, listing.)

Hold on to these verb strips and use them at different points during the following series of exploratory activities. Hold up one of the words from time to time to remind students of how they have been acting like scientists. Or display several of the words and ask students to select one that describes what they have just been doing.

Finally, introduce the explorations by reading the following statement:

We are going to explore a series of problems for which there are no obvious answers. The only way you will be able to find the answer is to try many experiments. Don't be afraid to make mistakes . . . learn from them.

Teacher Notes

1. Exploring Arrangements of Four Squares

Students will experiment to find out how many ways they can arrange four squares.

Teacher Materials: Four 6-inch squares made of construction paper
Double-sided tape
Cutouts of the arrangements:

Student Materials: Four 1-inch squares of construction paper
Labsheet 1 or 1/2-inch grid paper (Square Grid 2, page 150)

Getting Started

Place double-sided tape on the back of each of the four 6-inch squares. Then press the squares on a wall or the chalkboard to demonstrate this arrangement:

YES!

Point out to students that when they are arranging their squares, at least one edge of each square must match up with one edge of another square. Use the squares to demonstrate these two unacceptable arrangements:

NO!

NO!

Exploring the Problem

Pass out the student materials. Allow time for students to move the squares around on their desktops to make as many different arrangements as they can.

Don't be in a hurry. Exploring takes time. Keep asking students questions about their results. Continuously encourage students to evaluate their responses. Keep this time positive, receptive, and playful. Encourage students to take risks with their answers. Reinforce open responses. Give a lot of compliments. Show students that you value their responses. Urge them on. Get excited about what they are doing.

Have students record their arrangements on the labsheet or grid paper. Don't formalize the activity by collecting the labsheets for grading. That might inhibit responses.

Follow-up

Encourage students to share some of their solutions with the class. Draw their solutions on the chalkboard or invite students to do so. Accept all answers without evaluating them. Give students time to find the incorrect solutions. It is important for students to have an opportunity to evaluate the collected data.

If students do not find all the incorrect or duplicate solutions, ask the following questions to help them complete the evaluation:

- *Do all of the solutions have four squares?*
- *Do all of the squares in each solution have at least one edge that matches up with an edge of another square?*
- *Are there any duplicate solutions?*
- *Are there any missing solutions?*

If students think that two solutions are different just because one is upside down, you may need to use the cutouts to demonstrate "turns" and "flips." Examples:

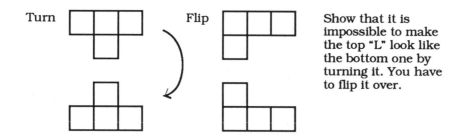

Turn

Flip

Show that it is impossible to make the top "L" look like the bottom one by turning it. You have to flip it over.

When students have completely evaluated the solution set, announce:

There are five, and only five, ways to arrange four squares so that all of the squares have at least one edge that matches up with an edge of another square.

Solution Set:

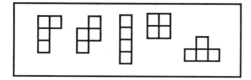

Note: You may want to have students save their recorded solutions for use with the next activity.

Independent Exploration

☐ ☐ ☐ ☐

If students will be working independently rather than having you guide them through the experiment, be sure to provide them with a copy of Labsheet 1. Follow up the independent work with a group discussion in which students share their solutions. This will help them to discover any arrangements they have missed and to identify any incorrect solutions. Finally, allow them to compare their solution sets with the five arrangements shown above.

Exploring Arrangements of Four Squares

Need: Four 1-inch squares of construction paper

Make drawings to record the arrangements you find.

Compare your solution set with those of other students.

2. Sorting Arrangements of Four Squares

Students will sort the five arrangements of four squares into two categories: regular and irregular.

Teacher Materials: Large representations of the five arrangements of four squares (see previous activity)
Double-sided tape

Getting Started

If you are working with younger students, you may need to begin by reviewing the characteristics of squares and rectangles. You also may need to reinforce the concept of *irregular* shapes by drawing several on the chalkboard. Examples:

(To avoid illustrating any of the shapes that students will be sorting in this activity, do not draw any shapes that are made up of four squares.)

The distinction between regular and irregular may not seem relevant or important now, but it will become important in the cube experiments that come later. Also, using this distinction is a good way to introduce a rule for sorting collected data.

Exploring the Problem

Place double-sided tape on the back of the arrangements of four squares that you will use in this activity. Then copy this chart onto the chalkboard, making each column large enough to accommodate at least three of the arrangements:

Regular	Irregular

Remind students of the five arrangements of four squares that they discovered in the previous activity. Hold up each one so that students can see it. Then ask:

• *Which of these shapes are regular?*
• *Which of these shapes are irregular?*

Invite students to come up and place each arrangement in the correct column of the chart. Encourage the class to evaluate each response. Have students tell why they think the shape does or does not belong in the column where it has been posted.

Solution Set:

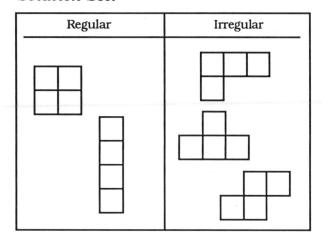

Follow-up

At this point, you may wish to refer students to the posted list of behavioral verbs (see "Setting the Stage" on page *xii*) and ask them to tell which of the verbs describe ways in which they have been acting like scientists in this and the previous activity. Example responses:

> *Experimenting* with arrangements of squares.
>
> *Collecting* solutions.
>
> *Testing* solutions to be sure that all the squares share at least one edge with another square.
>
> *Sorting* arrangements according to whether or not they are regular.

Note: Continue to emphasize the behavioral verbs throughout all of the activities in this book.

Independent Exploration

If students are to complete this activity on their own, they will need:

> a copy of Labsheet 2
>
> 1/2-inch grid paper (or the bottom of Labsheet 1)
>
> scissors and paste

Students will need to cut out the five arrangements of four squares. If students need to save the time it would take to redraw the arrangements, just have them cut out the drawings they made during the previous activity.

Encourage students to complete the chart on Labsheet 2 before comparing their solutions with those of other students. You may want to display some of the completed charts and have students evaluate them as part of a class discussion. Then have the class discuss specific ways they have been acting like scientists in these activities.

Sorting Arrangements of Four Squares

Need: 1/2-inch grid paper (or the bottom of Labsheet 1), scissors, paste

Cut out the five arrangements of four squares.

If an arrangement of squares does not form a rectangle or square, then it is irregular.

regular

irregular

Which of these arrangements are regular? Which are irregular?

Sort out the five arrangements and paste them on this chart.

Regular	Irregular

Compare your chart with those of other students.

EXPLORING WITH SQUARES AND CUBES
© Dale Seymour Publications

3. Exploring Arrangements of Five Squares ☐ ☐ ☐ ☐ ☐

Students will experiment to find out how many ways they can arrange five squares.

Teacher Materials: Five 6-inch squares made of construction paper, with double-sided tape on the back

Student Materials: Labsheet 3 (or 1/2-inch grid paper)
Thirty-five 1-inch squares of dark construction paper
Three sheets of white construction paper
Scissors and paste
One empty tissue box to collect data from the class

Getting Started

Review the results of Exploration 1 in which students arranged four squares. (There are five ways to arrange four squares.) Then ask:

How many ways do you think you can arrange five squares?

Use the five 6-inch squares to demonstrate this arrangement:

Encourage students to predict how many arrangements are possible *before* they begin the exploration. Use the 6-inch squares to demonstrate that there is only one way to arrange two squares and only two ways to arrange three squares:

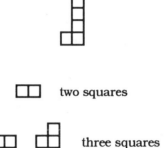

two squares

three squares

Copy this chart onto the chalkboard and have students predict what number will replace the question mark:

Number of Squares	Number of Arrangements
2	1
3	2
4	5
5	?

If necessary, review the rule that says at least one side of each square must share an edge with another square.

Exploring the Problem

There are two parts to this exploration. The first part involves exploring arrangements and the second part involves collecting data. It usually works best not to distribute the materials for the second part until after students have completed the first part.

Pass out five 1-inch squares to each student. Allow students time to discover several arrangements of five squares. Encourage students to record the arrangements they find on their labsheets or grid paper.

After several minutes, distribute the white construction paper, paste, and scissors. Ask students to paste down their five squares on the white paper in one of the arrangements they have recorded. Then have students cut out the arrangements, leaving a 1/4-inch border, and put them in the collection box.

Pass out another thirty squares to each student. Instruct students to continue pasting down arrangements of five squares, cutting them out, and putting them in the collection box. Accept all solutions, even duplicates. Begin posting solutions on the bulletin board while students are still contributing them to the collection box. Be sure to post some incorrect arrangements and duplicates. Pin some of the duplicates upside down or sideways. Allow students to find the mistakes.

Follow-up

When you have posted all of the solutions in the collection box, posting just two or three of the neatest ones for solutions with many duplicates, help students evaluate the data by asking them the following questions:

- *Do all the squares in each solution share at least one edge with another square?*
- *Are there any duplicates? (Check for flips and turns.)*
- *Are there any missing solutions?*

If students did not find all the arrangements for five squares, give them ten additional squares so that they can explore further. Continue collecting and evaluating arrangements until you have a complete solution set. Then announce:

There are twelve and only twelve possible arrangements for five squares. These shapes are called "pentominoes." Penta means "five."

Compare this result with any predictions students made before they began the exploration.

Solution Set:

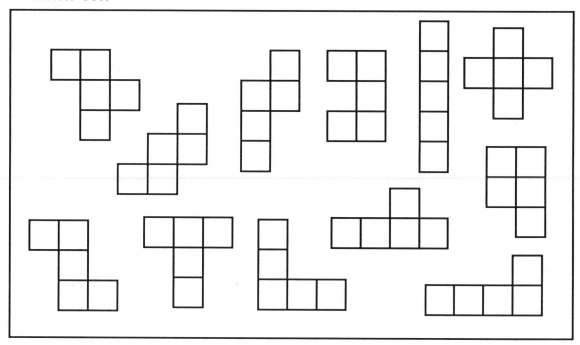

Note: Save a complete set of twelve pentominoes for use with Exploration 19.

Independent Exploration

If students are to complete this activity on their own, they can follow the procedures as outlined on Labsheet 3. Be sure students have an opportunity to compare their results with other students. Then discuss students' results with the class to evaluate the solutions and come up with the conclusion that there are twelve and only twelve pentominoes.

Exploring Arrangements of Five Squares

Step 1   Need: Five 1-inch squares of dark construction paper

Step 2   Need: About thirty 1-inch squares of dark construction paper, three sheets of white construction paper, scissors, paste

EXPLORING WITH SQUARES AND CUBES
© Dale Seymour Publications

Teacher Notes

4. Exploring Pentominoes

☐ ☐ ☐ ☐ ☐

Students will use pentominoes to fill the area of a 3 × 5 rectangle and a 4 × 5 rectangle.

Teacher Materials: A set of demonstration pentominoes, made from the patterns on pages 15 and 16

Student Materials: Pentomino patterns on pages 15 and 16
Scissors
Rectangles Puzzle Sheet on page 17
Several sheets of scratch paper
An envelope

Getting Started

Hold up the pentominoes (1) and (2) and show how they fit together:

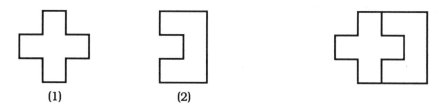

(1)   (2)

Invite a student to choose two other pentominoes that make the same shape. Example solutions:

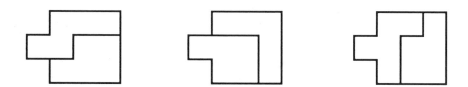

Point out that there are usually several, if not many, ways to combine pentominoes to fill a given area.

Exploring the Problem

There are four steps to this exploration. The first step is to have students cut out the pentominoes. Caution students to cut out the pentominoes very carefully. The pentominoes need to fit together like the pieces of a jigsaw puzzle.

The second step is to have students use the pentominoes to fill in each of the two rectangles on the puzzle sheet. Students should work on one rectangle at a time and can use the same pentominoes for the second rectangle that they used for the first. For younger students, who may be confused by having the two rectangles on the same puzzle sheet, cut the page in half. Pass out the 3 x 5 rectangle first and the 4 × 5 rectangle a little later.

Next have students record their solutions by tracing each pentomino in its place on the puzzle sheet. Younger students may need to work in pairs to complete the tracing. (One student can hold the pentomino in place while the other student traces.) Allow students time to compare their solutions with each other.

For the last step in this exploration, give each student several sheets of scratch paper. Then ask:

- *How many ways can you fill in the 3 × 5 rectangle?*
- *How many ways can you fill in the 4 × 5 rectangle?*

Encourage students to fill in the rectangles several different ways and trace each solution on a separate sheet of paper. Be sure to have extra scratch paper on hand for the few students who will get carried away and want to find *all* the possible solutions. Encourage students to post their solutions on the bulletin board and compare them with others.

Follow-up

When students have posted all their solutions, have them evaluate the collected data. If students have difficulty seeing the posted solutions from their desks, distribute copies of the Answer Keys on pages 18 and 19. Encourage students to look for duplicate solutions. Also have them look for solutions in which the same piece has been traced twice. Then ask:

- *What patterns do you see in the shapes used to fill the rectangles?*
- *Which shapes cannot be used? Why?*

See the following page for patterns students may suggest.

You may also want to ask students whether it is possible to fill in two 4 × 5 rectangles at the same time. (One way students could answer this question would be to examine the posted solutions for the 4 × 5 rectangle and see if there are any two that do not use any of the same pentominoes.)

Note: Have students store the pentominoes in envelopes so that they can use them in future explorations.

Independent Exploration   ☐ ☐ ☐ ☐ ☐

If students are to complete this activity on their own, they can follow the procedures as outlined on Labsheet 4. Be sure they have an opportunity to post their solutions and compare them with those of other students. Then help students evaluate the data by having them eliminate duplicate and incorrect solutions and then discuss any patterns they see.

cannot be used because they divide
the area into two equivalent "leftovers."

cannot be used because it leaves an area that
can only be divided into two equivalent areas.

cannot be used because it always leaves
a notch in the corner.

cannot be used in a corner because it leaves
a notch. It cannot be used in the middle
because it leaves an area that is symmetrical,
and two of the three pentominoes required to
fill it would have to be identical.

Exploring Pentominoes

Need: A copy of the twelve pentomino patterns, scissors, a copy of the rectangles puzzle sheet, several sheets of scratch paper

1 Carefully cut out the twelve pentomino pieces.

2 Choose pentominoes to fill in the two rectangles.

You do not have to fill them both at the same time.

After completing one, you can use the pieces over again to fill in the other.

3 When you have filled in a rectangle, trace each pentomino in its place to make a record of your solution.

Compare your rectangles with those of other students.

How many ways can you fill in the 4 x 5 rectangle?

Try several ways, tracing each answer on a separate sheet of paper.

Post your answers on the bulletin board. Compare yours with others already there.

4

Are there any pentominoes that cannot be used in filling the rectangles? Why?

When you finish, store your pentominoes in the envelope. Don't seal it! Save them for the next experiment.

Pentomino Patterns

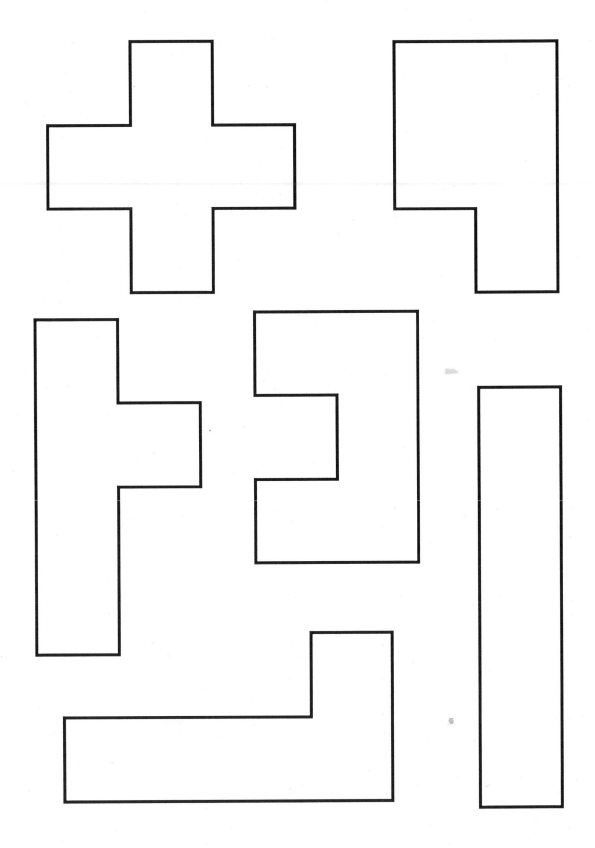

3 × 5

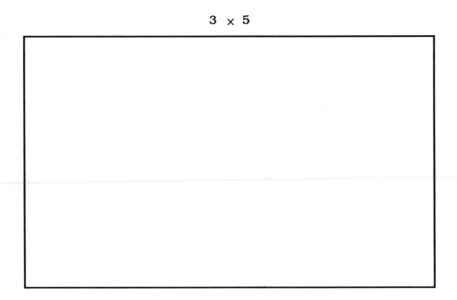

4 × 5

3 × 5

EXPLORING WITH SQUARES AND CUBES
© Dale Seymour Publications

4 × 5

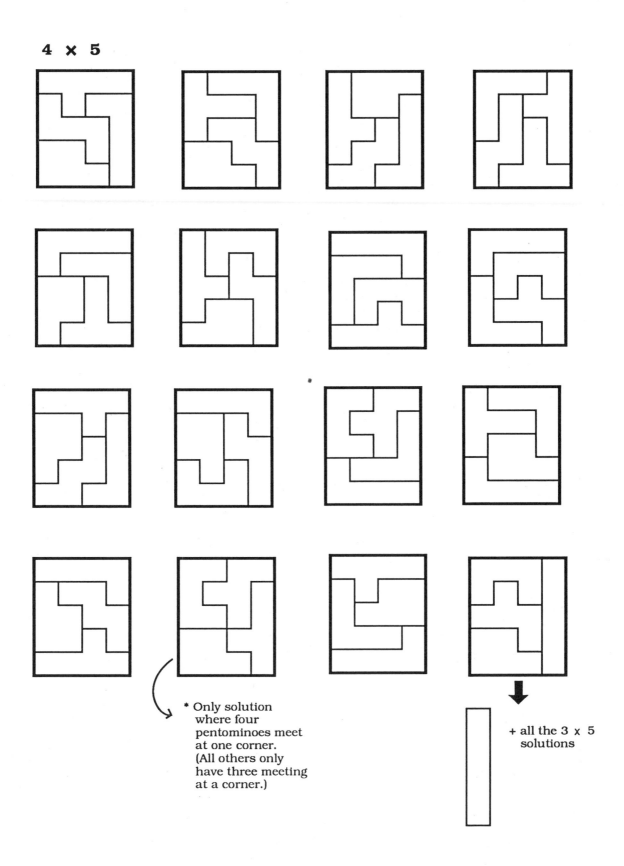

* Only solution
where four
pentominoes meet
at one corner.
(All others only
have three meeting
at a corner.)

+ all the 3 x 5
solutions

5. Making Pentomino Puzzles

□ □ □ □ □

Students will make their own pentomino puzzles for other students to solve.

Teacher Materials: Set of demonstration pentominoes
Student Materials: Set of pentominoes
Several sheets of scratch paper

Getting Started

Combine the pentominoes (1) and (2) to form this shape:

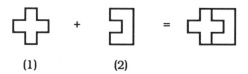

(1)   (2)

Hold these two pentominoes against the chalkboard and trace the outline with a piece of chalk. Then remove the two pentominoes so that students can see the outline. Ask students to suggest names for the shape. Examples:

•profile of a man with a square nose
fly swatter without its handle
coffee cup with a small handle

short tree
top view of a man with a square nose
a square bottle upside down

Invite students to use the demonstration pentominoes to show some different ways this shape can be filled in with pentominoes. Example solutions:

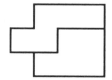 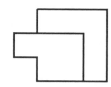 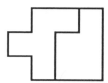

Exploring the Problem

Have students use pentominoes to make their own puzzles on the sheets of scratch paper. Remind them to make the outline by tracing around the outside of the shape only. Once students have outlined their puzzle shapes, be sure to have them write names for the shapes. Examples of four pentomino puzzles appear on pages 27–30.

Encourage students to use just three or four pentominoes when making their first puzzle. (Some students try to use all twelve pentominoes and become frustrated when they end up with a large irregular shape that they cannot name.) Working toward a recognizable shape forces students to look carefully at how the pieces can fit together in certain combinations.

Have students give their puzzles to someone else to solve. Make sure that all students have the opportunity to solve someone else's puzzle. An alternative to having students exchange puzzles is to collect the puzzles, copy them, and make a pentomino puzzle book authored by the class. Then students can use their pentominoes to solve all the puzzles in the book.

Most of the puzzle shapes students make will be irregular. After students have made and solved at least one puzzle, encourage them to make some different-sized square and rectangle puzzles.

Follow-up

Students occasionally create puzzles that are impossible to solve. If that occurs, have students explore the reasons for it. Usually the student has traced the outline incorrectly, adding or subtracting area. Or, if the shape has a hole in it, the student may have forgotten to trace the hole.

Independent Exploration   ☐ ☐ ☐ ☐ ☐

Students can complete this activity on their own by following the procedures described on Labsheet 5. Have students work in pairs or small groups so that they will be able to trade puzzles. If students create any puzzles that are impossible to solve, help them discover the reasons for it.

Making Pentomino Puzzles

Need: One set of pentominoes, several sheets of scratch paper

6. Evaluating Irregular Pentomino Puzzles □ □ □ □ □

Students will fill in pentomino puzzles with squares and then determine how many pentominoes it would take to fill the puzzles.

Teacher Materials: Pentomino puzzle on page 27 (or an unsolved puzzle from Exploration 5)

Twenty 7/8-inch squares with double-sided tape on the back (You can use Square Grid 3, page 151, to make the squares. Also, you may need more or fewer squares if you are using one of the unsolved puzzles.)

Student Materials: Three pentomino puzzles (unsolved puzzles created by students or the three puzzles on pages 28, 29, and 30)

Forty to fifty 7/8-inch squares

Getting Started

Copy this chart onto the chalkboard:

Puzzle name	Number of squares	Number of pentominoes

Then demonstrate how to find the area of a pentomino puzzle by filling it in with squares. Begin at the top of the puzzle and press on the 7/8-inch squares in rows. Encourage students to notice how you do not overlap the squares or leave gaps between them. Example:

Have students count the squares you use to fill in the entire puzzle. Then write "house" and "20" in the appropriate spaces of the first row of the chart on the chalkboard. (You will have a different puzzle name and number of squares if you are using an unsolved puzzle from Exploration 5.)

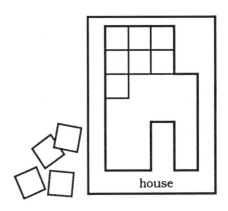

house

Exploring the Problem

Pass out the puzzles and 7/8-inch squares to students. Ask students to fill in each of the puzzles with the squares. After completely filling each puzzle, students should count the number of squares used and record that number somewhere on the puzzle sheet. Then they can reuse the squares to fill in the next puzzle. Some students may want to save time by just drawing in lines to count squares. Encourage these students to use a ruler for accuracy.

After students have found the area of all three puzzles, have them help you fill in the first two columns of the chart on the chalkboard. Then ask:

> *How many pentomino pieces would it take to fill in the house?*

Don't be in a hurry to answer this question if students don't come up with the answer immediately. Remind students that *penta* means "five." After discussion, solicit the rule "Divide by five." Then have students use this rule to determine how many pentominoes would be needed to fill in each of the other puzzles. (Some students may want to use their pentominoes to try to solve the three puzzles.) Complete the last column of the chart.

Puzzle name	Number of squares	Number of pentominoes
house	20	4
dinosaur	25	5
robot face	40	8
tree	35	7

Follow-up

You may wish to point out to students that they have been acting like scientists by *measuring* area. If some students had the opportunity to use their pentominoes to solve the puzzles, they were also *testing* the data in the last column of the chart. Encourage students to choose other behavioral verbs (see "Setting the Stage," page *xii*) to describe other aspects of the experiment.

If you have used unsolved puzzles from Exploration 5, you may find some with areas that are not multiples of 5. If this happens, ask:

> *What if a puzzle has an area that cannot be divided evenly by 5?*

If students seem to hesitate, resist the temptation to give them the answer. Give them time to figure out that a puzzle with an area that cannot be divided evenly by 5 cannot be filled completely with pentominoes.

Puzzle Solutions:

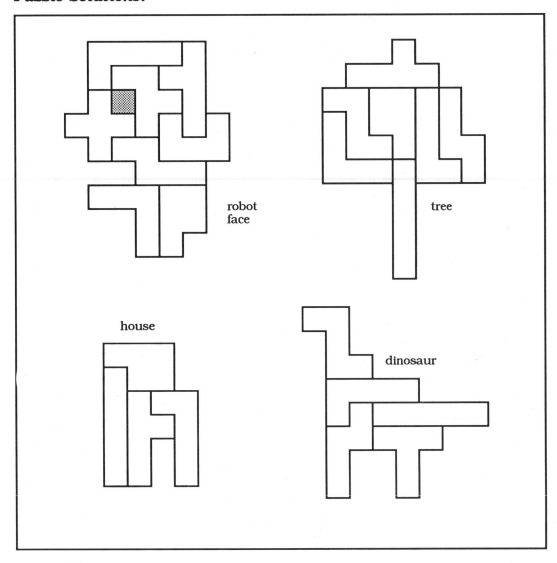

robot
face

tree

house

dinosaur

Independent Exploration

□ □ □ □ □

Students can complete this activity on their own by following the procedures described on Labsheet 6. If you need to demonstrate how to fill in a puzzle with squares, you can partially fill in the house puzzle and then refer students to the labsheet to see how many squares are needed in all. Conclude the activity by using behavioral verbs to discuss with students how they have been acting like scientists.

Evaluating Irregular Pentomino Puzzles

Need: Forty 7/8-inch squares of paper, three pentomino puzzles

Use the squares to fill in the puzzle.

Count the number of squares you used to fill in the puzzle.

Write the number of squares on the chart.

Puzzle name	Number of squares	Number of pentominoes
house	20	

Do the same thing for the other puzzles.

How many pentominoes would it take to fill in each puzzle?

Write those amounts on the chart.

How did you find the number of pentominoes needed to fill in each puzzle?

Save the puzzles. Later you can try to fill them in with pentominoes.

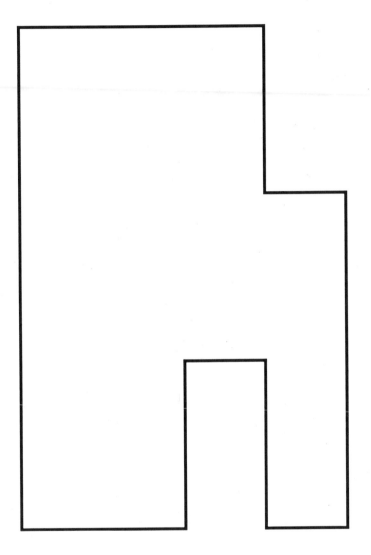

house

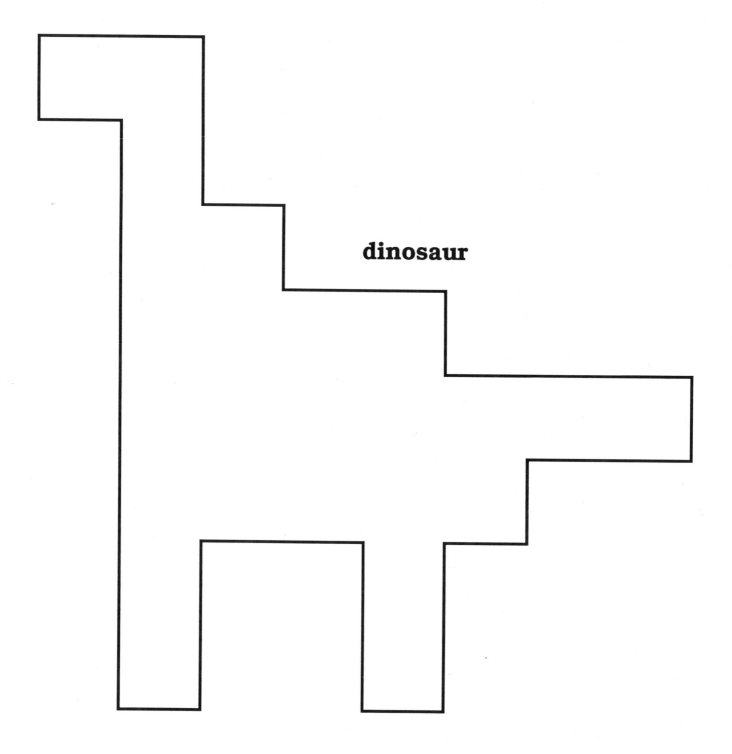

dinosaur

EXPLORING WITH SQUARES AND CUBES
© Dale Seymour Publications

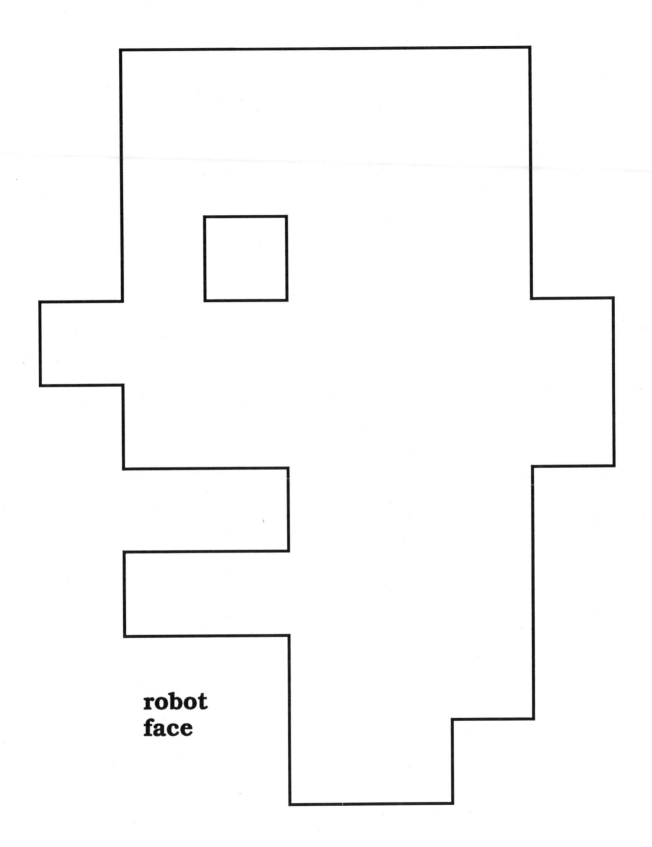

**robot
face**

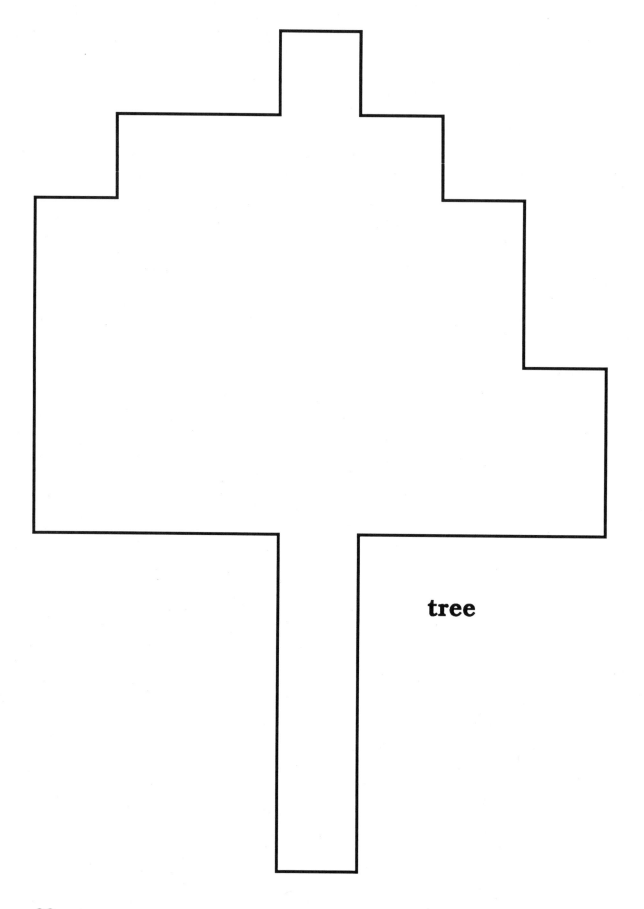

tree

7. Evaluating Regular Pentomino Puzzles   ☐ ☐ ☐ ☐ ☐

Students will find all the rectangles that can be completely filled in with pentominoes.

Teacher Materials: Set of demonstration pentominoes with double-side tape on the back

Student Materials: Several sheets of 7/8-inch grid paper (Square Grid 3, page 151)
Scissors
Set of pentominoes

Getting Started

Have students think back to the exploration in which they made pentomino puzzles. Ask how many students were able to make puzzles in the shape of a square. If any students did make square puzzles, ask them to tell what size squares they made. Then ask:

> *How many different-sized squares can you make with pentominoes?*

If students cannot tell you how many squares are possible, encourage them to think about the problem systematically. One approach is to list all the square numbers between 1 and 60 (the area of the largest possible pentomino puzzle) and see which are multiples of 5. Students will soon see that a 5 × 5 square is the only square that can be filled with pentominoes because 25 is the only square number that is a multiple of 5.

Exploring the Problem

This exploration is divided into two steps. In step 1 students collect rectangles that have areas between 0 and 60 and are multiples of 5. In step 2 students test the rectangles to see if they can be filled with pentominoes.

For step 1 students will need the 7/8-inch grid paper (Square Grid 3) and scissors. Ask:

> *How many rectangles can you find that have areas between 0 and 60 that are multiples of 5?*

Have students cut out several such rectangles and post them on the bulletin board. (Students may need more than one sheet of grid paper to create some of the larger rectangles.) Students will undoubtedly post the rectangles in haphazard order. Encourage students to examine the collection of rectangles and identify and remove all the duplicates.

Then ask students to determine if there are any rectangles that haven't been posted yet. This can be difficult to do when the data is disorganized. Have students explore ways to sort the rectangles into groups (by area, perimeter, or length and width).

Organizing the Rectangles by Length and Width:

1 x 5	1 x 10	1 x 15	1 x 20	1 x 25	1 x 30	1 x 35	1 x 40	1 x 45	1 x 50	1 x 55	1 x 60
2 x 5	2 x 10	2 x 15	2 x 20	2 x 25	2 x 30						
3 x 5	3 x 10	3 x 15	3 x 20								
4 x 5	4 x 10	4 x 15									
5 x 5	5 x 10*										
6 x 5	6 x 10										
7 x 5											
8 x 5											
9 x 5											
10 x 5*			* Duplicate rectangles								
11 x 5											
12 x 5											

Sorting by length and width gives the most useful pattern. If there are any gaps in the pattern, then a rectangle is missing. Have several students cut out the missing rectangles and add them to the collection. Students also may find that some of the rectangles they have posted do not have areas that are multiples of 5. Remove those rectangles from the collection.

Students should now take out their pentominoes for step 2 of the exploration. Have students take rectangles from the bulletin board and see if they can cover them completely with pentominoes. If they can, have them trace the solution on the rectangle and post it again.

If students cannot find a solution, have them post the rectangle in a section of the bulletin board designated for rectangles that are impossible to solve. Some students may want to challenge the posting of rectangles in that section by trying to find solutions for them. After all the rectangles have been solved or posted in the "impossible to solve" section, have students examine the rectangles without solutions and describe any patterns or general characteristics they see.

Follow-up

At this point it may be helpful to sort the pentominoes by their widths and then use the results to continue analyzing the rectangles that are impossible to solve. Copy this chart on the chalkboard:

One square wide	Two squares wide	Three squares wide

Invite students to press the demonstration pentominoes onto the board in the correct columns of the chart.

Solution Set:

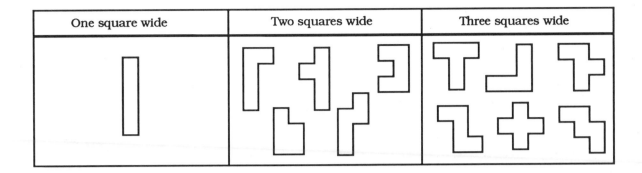

One square wide	Two squares wide	Three squares wide

Encourage students to look again at the rectangles that are impossible to solve and state reasons why those rectangles do not have solutions.

Example Responses:

This is too long and too narrow. (There aren't enough pentominoes that are one square wide.)

This can be filled with duplicate pieces only.

There aren't enough pentominoes two squares wide that can be used to fill this rectangle. This shape cannot be used because of the notch.

You may want to point out to students that they are acting like scientists when they *analyze* and *identify* patterns or similar characteristics in a body of collected data.

Note: These activities, and those to come, will take many days and/or weeks to complete. Move at a pace that is appropriate for your students. Don't be in a hurry. Take the time needed to explore in detail. Ask students many questions concerning relationships, comparisons, etc. *Don't hesitate to ask questions for which you don't know the answers. . . .* Enjoy the "idea play" with students. Explore with them. *You don't have to know the answer to ask the question!*

Independent Exploration ☐ ☐ ☐ ☐ ☐

Students can complete this activity on their own by following the procedures described on Labsheet 7. Have students work in small groups to find all the rectangles, test them for pentomino solutions, and discuss the results. As a follow-up, work with the whole group to make a chart that sorts the pentominoes by width and use this information to determine why certain rectangles are impossible to solve.

MATHEMATICS DEPARTMENT
ALVERNO COLLEGE
MILWAUKEE, WI 53234-3922

Evaluating Regular Pentomino Puzzles

| Step 1 | Need: 7/8-inch grid paper and scissors |

| Step 2 | Need: One set of pentominoes |

8. Designing Pentomino Puzzles (I) □ □ □ □ □

Students will invent a symmetrical shape with an area equal to 60 square units and then see if it can be completely filled in with all twelve pentominoes.

Student Materials: One sheet of 1/4-inch grid paper (Square Grid 1, page 149)

Set of pentominoes

Copy of the puzzle shape on page 37

Getting Started

This exploration and Exploration 9 are the *inverse* of Exploration 5. In Exploration 5 students began with pentominoes and used them to construct a puzzle shape. Here students first come up with a shape and then test it to see if it can be filled in with pentominoes.

Review the equation that gives the total area that can be covered by all twelve pentominoes: $5 \times 12 = 60$. Then ask:

> *What is the largest possible symmetrical puzzle shape for all twelve pentominoes?*

Exploring the Problem

Most students will answer the question about the largest shape that can be covered with the twelve pentominoes by citing one of the rectangles from Exploration 7 that was posted and proved to have a solution. For example, students might cite the 5 × 12 rectangle or the 6 × 10 rectangle. Suggest a square that is 8 × 8. Give students the opportunity to point out that the square is too large by 4 square units.

Have students use their grid paper to draw *symmetrical* shapes that have an area of 60 square units and which they think could be filled with the twelve pentominoes. Invite them also to draw an 8 × 8 square and take out four squares so that the area of the shape becomes equal to 60.

After ten or fifteen minutes, ask students to share some of their shapes with the class. Hold up their papers or draw some of the shapes on the chalkboard so that other students can see them. Have the class compute the area of each shape to see if is indeed 60.

Example Solutions for Modified 8 x 8 Squares:

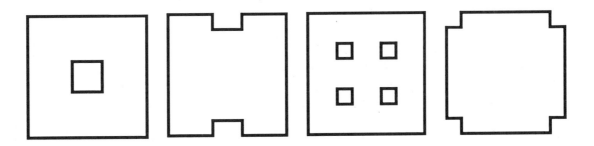

If it has not already been shown, draw the square with the corners removed on the chalkboard. Then give a copy of this puzzle shape to each student. Invite students to try to fill in the puzzle with *all* twelve pentominoes.

This is a very difficult puzzle. Very few students will solve it, but it is worth the effort. You may even find that some parents of your students will get involved in trying to solve this puzzle.

Follow-up

Some students will begin to exhibit frustration because of the difficulty of this puzzle. Provide some hints by revealing part of the solution. For example, draw this much on the board or tell students which six pentominoes will fill exactly half the puzzle without showing them how.

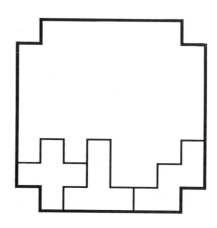

Encourage students to try to solve some of the other shapes they have drawn. Note that students may need to copy the shapes onto 7/8-inch grid paper (Square Grid 3, page 151) before attempting to solve them with their pentominoes. Start a collection of solutions on the bulletin board.

Solution:

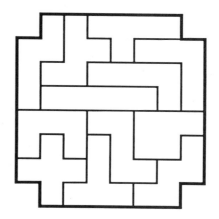

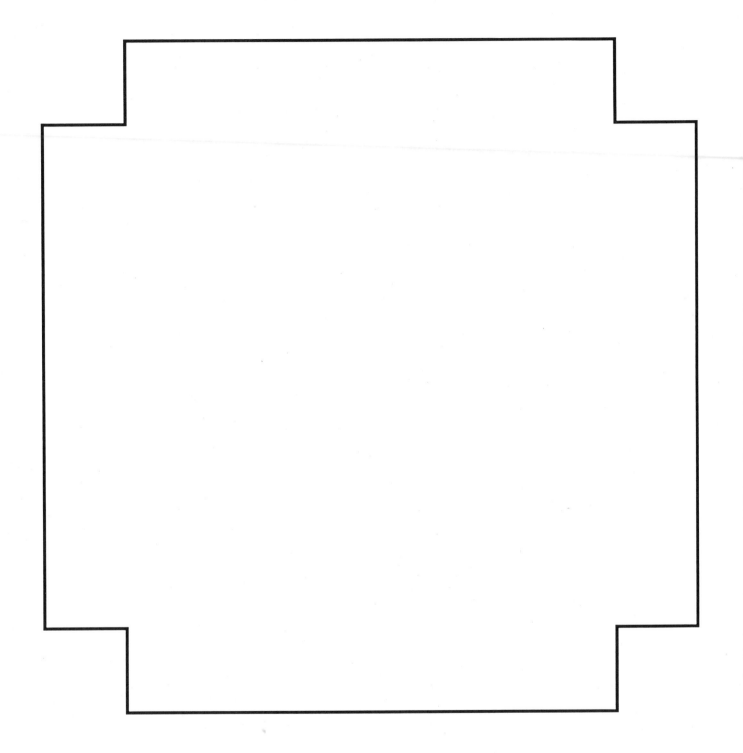

9. Designing Pentomino Puzzles (II)

Students will create pentomino puzzle shapes that either are symmetrical or are squares or rectangles with holes or notches in them.

Student Materials: Three or four sheets of 7/8-inch grid paper
                      Set of pentominoes

Getting Started

Review the concept of symmetry. Show students that a shape is symmetrical if you can draw a line through the center of the shape and have both halves look the same.

Then remind students that the only square that can be completely filled with pentominoes is the 5 × 5 square (see Exploration 7). Any other square needs to have some area taken out to make its area equal to a multiple of 5. Taking out the area from a square creates a shape that has either holes or notches. Examples:

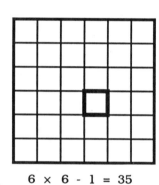

6 × 6 - 1 = 35

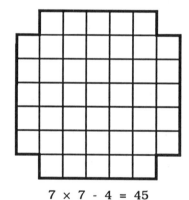

7 × 7 - 4 = 45

The same is true for rectangles with areas that are not multiples of 5.

Exploring the Problem

Have students draw shapes on their grid paper that can be filled in with pentominoes. Remind them that each shape must have an area that is a multiple of 5. Encourage students to make some of the shapes symmetrical. Encourage them also to create shapes by making holes or notches in squares or rectangles. The range of possible shapes and sizes is suggested by the examples on page 40. Some larger shapes may require students to tape two sheets of grid paper together. For example, the shape to the right.

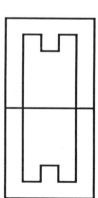

After students have drawn several shapes, have them test the shapes by trying to fill them in with pentominoes. (Otherwise some students will get carried away and draw lots of shapes without testing any of them.) If students discover shapes that cannot be filled in, encourage them to figure out why (see Exploration 4). Then have them modify the shapes so that they can be filled in.

Invite students to trade shapes and try to solve each other's puzzles. Be sure that every student has the opportunity to participate. An alternative to having students trade puzzles is to post all the puzzles on the bulletin board and have students select which puzzles they want to solve. This activity becomes an informal evaluation in which students determine whether or not the shapes they have made can be filled in with pentominoes.

For the second part of this activity, have students use the grid paper to outline the first letter of their last name. Remind them to outline an area that is a multiple of 5. Then have students try to fill in the letters with pentominoes. Students may need to modify the outlines if they cannot fill the letters as originally drawn. (You may need to refer to Exploration 4 to help students evaluate their outlines.)

Example Letter Solutions:

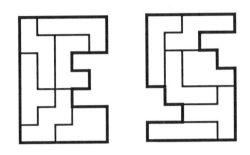

Follow-up

Post the puzzles students have solved on the bulletin board. If there are some puzzles that have been declared impossible to solve, have the class analyze why those puzzles do not have solutions.

You may want to have the class sort the shapes and post the solutions in groups. You could, for example, have them post the shapes on a chart like the one below. Sorting the shapes this way may reveal patterns that suggest some shapes students have overlooked.

Holes		Notches		Holes and Notches	
SQUARES	RECTANGLES	SQUARES	RECTANGLES	SQUARES	RECTANGLES

Students might also enjoy posting the solutions for the letter puzzles in an alphabet across the front of the room.

Independent Exploration

☐ ☐ ☐ ☐ ☐

If you want to have students work more independently, distribute copies of Labsheet 9. Encourage students to read the instructions carefully. This activity will work best if students work in pairs or small groups so that they can trade puzzles and work together to figure out why some shapes cannot be solved.

Sample Shapes

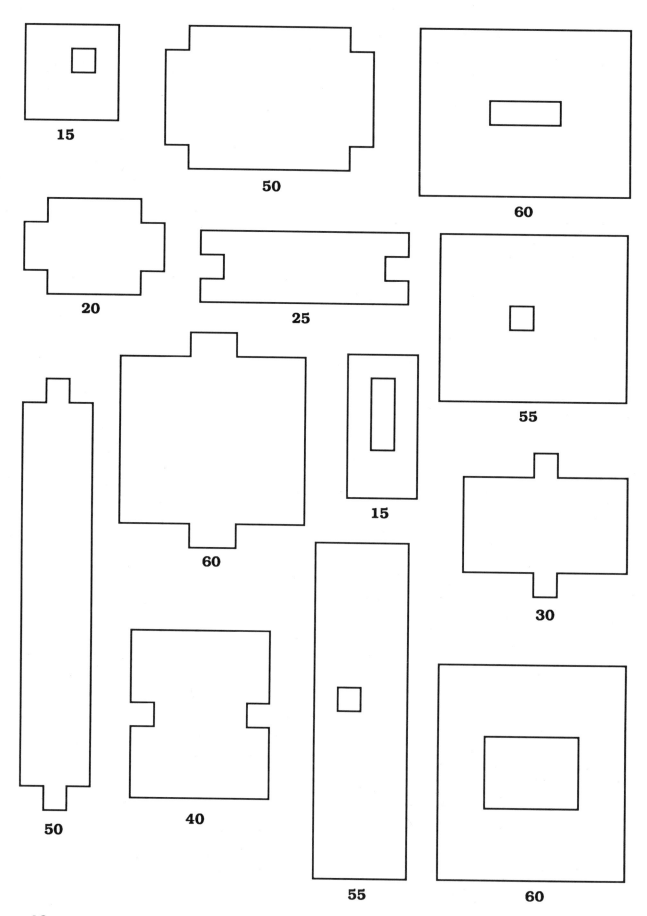

15

50

60

20

25

55

15

60

50

30

40

55

60

40

Designing Pentomino Puzzles (II)

Need: Three or four sheets of 7/8-inch grid paper, set of pentominoes

10. Sequencing Pentominoes ☐ ☐ ☐ ☐ ☐

Students will sequence the twelve pentominoes so that each pentomino can be made by moving one square in the preceding pentomino one square's distance.

Teacher Materials: Set of demonstration pentominoes with double-sided tape on the back

Student Materials: Set of pentominoes

A large sheet of scratch paper

Five 1-inch squares (optional)

Getting Started

Explain to students that sequencing is a way of ordering the members of a set according to a particular rule. A set of names, for example, can be put in alphabetical order. And a set of consecutive numbers can be put in counting order according to the rule $n + 1$. If students need specific examples, write some sets of names and numbers on the chalkboard and work with students to put them in alphabetical and numerical order.

Exploring the Problem

Press the first pentomino to the right onto the chalkboard. Then ask:

If you moved one square in this pentomino one square's distance, which pentomino would this one be changed into?

After students have had a chance to suggest an answer, press the second pentomino to the right onto the chalkboard and show how it is just like the preceding pentomino with one square moved. Draw an arrow between the two shapes. Then ask the same question about this pentomino that you asked about the first one.

Allow students to come up with several answers. Show that there may be more than one possibility for the next pentomino when sequencing the shapes according to this rule. See the examples on the facing page.

Then ask:

Is it possible to put all twelve pentominoes in a sequence according to this rule?

Allow students time to explore sequences of pentominoes by moving them around on their desktops. If some students find this task too abstract, allow them to manipulate five 1-inch squares while sequencing the pentominoes. If it would also help students to have the sequencing rule to refer to, write it on the chalkboard:

Move one square one square's distance.

Examples of Pentomino Sequences:

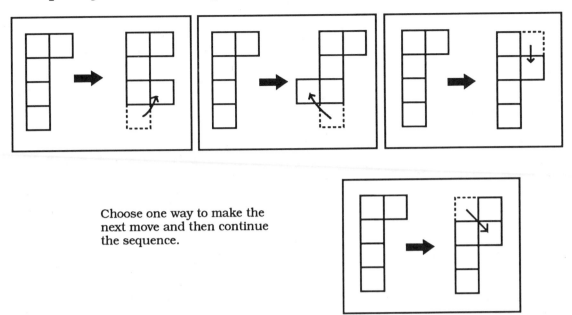

Choose one way to make the
next move and then continue
the sequence.

After students have found a complete sequence, have them record it by carefully tracing around each pentomino and drawing arrows to show the order. Most students will probably arrange the pentominoes in a linear sequence. Point out that it is also possible to create a branching sequence. (See page 44 for examples of both a linear and a branching sequence.) Encourage students to compare their solutions with those of other students. You may want to post students' solutions on the bulletin board.

Follow-up

Show several of the students' sequences and have the class evaluate them according to the sequencing rule. If the posted sequences are too small for students to see from their desks, make copies of several solutions and distribute them to the class. Then students can draw any corrections right on the incorrect sequences.

Independent Exploration   ☐ ☐ ☐ ☐ ☐

Some students may be able to complete this exploration independently by following the explanation given on Labsheet 10. If they have trouble completing a linear sequence, show them how to start a branching one. Be sure students have an opportunity to compare their sequences with those of other students. Encourage students to evaluate the sequences according to the sequencing rule.

Sequence Solutions for Pentominoes

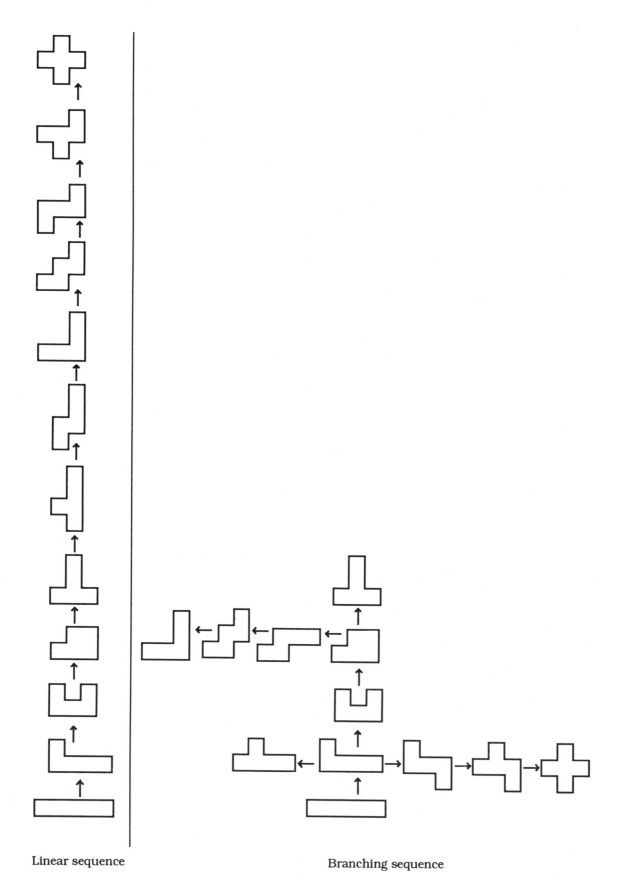

Linear sequence

Branching sequence

EXPLORING WITH SQUARES AND CUBES
© Dale Seymour Publications

Sequencing Pentominoes

Need: Set of pentominoes, large sheet of scratch paper

11. "Packing" or Tiling Pentominoes
(an optional art application)

□ □ □ □ □

Students will cover, or tile, an area with pentominoes by tracing the same shape again and again.

Teacher Materials: One demonstration pentomino: 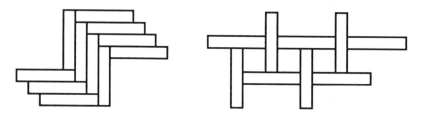

Student Materials: One pentomino

Art paper

Pencil and crayons

Getting Started

Explain to students that when tiling an area you normally try to cover it completely without leaving any holes or gaps. In this activity, however, they will be able to create any repeating pattern as long as it is made up of just one pentomino shape.

Use the demonstration pentomino to show how to create a repeating pattern. Trace the pentomino on the chalkboard, reposition it, and trace it again. Show one pattern that does not have holes and one pattern that does. Examples:

Point out that these patterns are "infinite." That is, students should be able to run these patterns off all edges of the paper.

Exploring the Problem

Instruct students to choose *one* pentomino and use it to create a repeating pattern. Students should use a pencil to trace the pentomino over and over again so that the pattern covers a sheet of art paper. Students can flip or turn the pentomino to create the pattern, but they should not overlap the tracings.

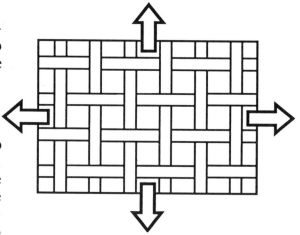

When students have finished tracing the pattern in pencil, have them choose two or three colors and create a color pattern within the line pattern. A design will be clearer if the same color is used to fill all the holes in the pattern. (This color is in addition to the colors used to fill in the pentomino tracings themselves.) An example appears on the facing page.

Sample Design:

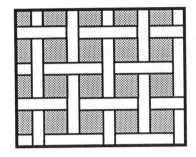

Post the completed designs and ask students to compare their results. Ask, for example:

- *How many different patterns can be created with the same pentomino?*

- *How does changing the color pattern change the design?*

Follow-up

Students may discover that some of the posted designs do not follow the rules given for creating them. Have students discuss those designs by asking these questions:

- *Has more than one pentomino been used to create the design?*

- *Does the pattern repeat itself infinitely?*

- *Does the design have a repeating color pattern?*

- *How many colors have been used?*

- *Do any of the pentomino tracings overlap?*

After discussing the patterns students have created, challenge them to test each pentomino to determine whether it can be used to tile an area without leaving any holes.

Then, for students interested in creating further designs, allow them to ignore the rules used above. See the variations shown on page 48. Students who invent variations of their own have moved into the level of thinking described by Bruner as "independent investigation." This is a goal that should be encouraged for all students.

Three Variations that "Break" the Rules

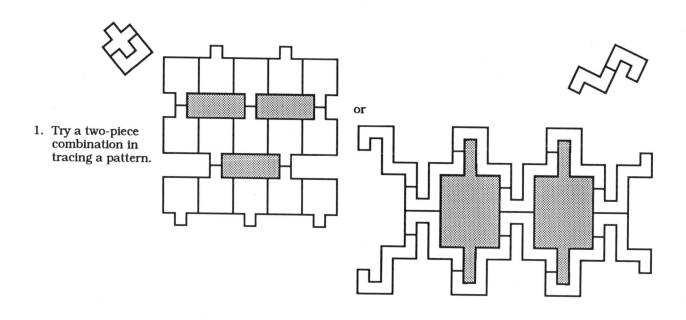

1. Try a two-piece combination in tracing a pattern.

or

2. Use two different pentominoes to trace a pattern.

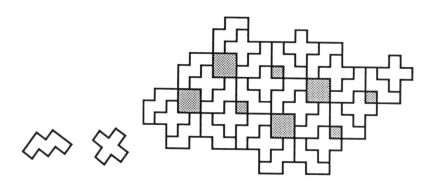

3. Try overlapping shapes while tracing the pattern.

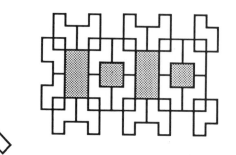

12. Exploring Arrangements of Six Squares □ □ □ □ □ □

Students will experiment to find out how many ways they can arrange six squares.

Student Materials: Labsheet 12 (or 1/2-inch grid paper)
About fifty 1-inch squares of dark construction paper
Six or seven sheets of white construction paper
Scissors and paste
One empty tissue box for data collection

Getting Started

Remind students of Exploration 3 in which they predicted how many ways they could arrange five squares. Then copy this chart onto the chalkboard and ask:

How many ways can you arrange six squares?

Have students predict how many arrangements are possible before they begin working with the squares. If necessary, remind them that all the squares in an arrangement must share at least one edge with another square.

Number of Squares	Number of Arrangements
2	1
3	2
4	5
5	12
6	?

Exploring the Problem

Each student will need six 1-inch squares for the first part of this exploration. Encourage students to begin exploring possible arrangements by moving the squares around on their desktops. Instruct students to record the arrangements on their labsheets or grid paper.

For the second part of this exploration, students will need white construction paper, paste, and scissors. Have students recall how they pasted down and cut out the arrangements of five squares in Exploration 3. Instruct them to do the same thing now with one of their arrangements of six squares. Remind them to leave a 1/4-inch border. Then have students put the cutout arrangements in the collection box.

Pass out another forty squares to each student so that the students can continue adding arrangements to the collection box. In the meantime you can begin to post solutions on the bulletin board. Try to post all the arrangements, even incorrect ones. Post duplicates so that they are flipped or turned. If an arrangement has many duplicates, just post two or three of the neatest ones.

Note that if the twelve pentominoes are still posted on the bulletin board, some students might use the shortcut of adding one square to a pentomino to form a hexomino. Don't point out this possibility to students . . . let them discover it!

Follow-up

Encourage students to evaluate the data as they did for the arrangements of five squares in Exploration 3. If necessary, prompt them with the following questions:

- *Do all of the arrangements have six squares?*
- *Do all the squares in each solution share at least one edge with another square?*
- *Are there any duplicates? (Check for flips and turns.)*
- *Are there any missing solutions?*

If students have not found all the possible arrangements, give them more squares and encourage them to continue exploring. Remind students that they may need to turn or flip their arrangements to see if they are indeed new solutions.

Once you have a complete solution set, announce:

> *There are thirty-five and only thirty-five arrangements for six squares. These shapes are call "hexominoes."*

Have students compare this result with any predictions they made at the beginning of this activity. The thirty-five arrangements are shown on pages 52 and 53. Students will cut out the patterns on these pages as part of Exploration 13.

Note: Save a complete set of thirty-five hexominoes for use with Exploration 19.

Independent Exploration

If students are to complete this activity on their own, they can follow the procedures as outlined on Labsheet 12. Allow students to work in small groups so that they can compare their arrangements with those of other students. Help students evaluate their data and make sure that each group reaches the final conclusion that there are thirty-five possible arrangements.

Note: At this point some students may take this series of explorations one step further and begin to construct *septominoes* (arrangements of seven squares). If they do, it is an excellent sign that they have moved from the level of problem solving to the level of independent investigation. Allow them to reach this level on their own. If you immediately suggest septominoes to them as an extension of this exploration, you will "short circuit" the "learning moment" and remove the possibility for students to think of it themselves.

Give the independent investigators space on the bulletin board to post their arrangements of seven squares. This may draw other students into the search. If they persevere, they will find 108 septominoes . . . please don't tell them.

Exploring Arrangements of Six Squares

Step 1 | Need: Six 1-inch squares of dark construction paper

Step 2 | Need: About forty 1-inch squares of dark construction paper, several sheets of white construction paper, scissors, paste

EXPLORING WITH SQUARES AND CUBES
© Dale Seymour Publications

13. Exploring Hexominoes   ☐ ☐ ☐ ☐ ☐ ☐

Students will use hexominoes to fill the area of 3 × 6 rectangles.

Student Materials: Hexomino patterns on pages 52 and 53
Scissors
Two copies of the Puzzle Sheet on page 57
An envelope

Getting Started

Remind students of the thirty-five hexominoes they discovered as part of Exploration 12. (If the arrangements are still posted on the bulletin board, call them to students' attention.)

Then show students a copy of the hexomino patterns that they are about to cut out. Caution students that they will have to cut out the hexominoes very carefully so that they will fit together like the pieces of a jigsaw puzzle. Encourage students to be patient as this task will take some time.

Finally, have students recall how there were many different ways to fill a given area with pentominoes. The same is true for hexominoes.

Exploring the Problem

After students have cut out all the hexominoes, ask them to use any three hexominoes to fill in one of the rectangles on the puzzle sheet. Have students record their solutions by tracing each hexomino in place. Encourage students to be neat in their tracing. If some students have trouble tracing the solutions, they can work in pairs so that one person can hold the hexominoes in place while the other person traces around them.

Have students continue to find as many other solutions as they can. Encourage students to compare their results with other students, but only after they have found ten solutions on their own.

The two puzzle sheets provide enough space to record twenty different solutions. There are twenty-one solutions to this problem (see page 58). Just in case any students get carried away and continue until they find all twenty-one solutions, you may want to cut up a puzzle sheet into individual rectangles that you can distribute as needed.

Follow-up

Each student will need a set of the twenty-one solutions. While some students may have persevered long enough to come up with a complete solution set on their own, you may need to distribute copies of the solutions shown on page 58. (Be sure not to show this page to students until all the solutions have been discovered by at least one person in the class.)

Discuss the solutions with students. Ask:

Which hexominoes could not be used to fill the rectangles? Why?

Encourage students to analyze the solutions carefully in order to answer the question.

54

Possible responses:

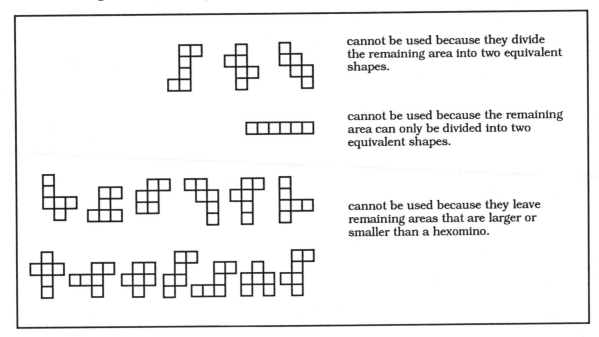

cannot be used because they divide the remaining area into two equivalent shapes.

cannot be used because the remaining area can only be divided into two equivalent shapes.

cannot be used because they leave remaining areas that are larger or smaller than a hexomino.

Note: Have students store the hexominoes in envelopes so that they can use them in future explorations.

Independent Exploration

☐ ☐ ☐ ☐ ☐ ☐

If students are to complete this activity on their own, they can follow the procedures as outlined on Labsheet 13. You may want to have students work in pairs or small groups so that they can compare their arrangements with each other. After students have had a reasonable amount of time to work on their own, encourage them to evaluate their data to see if they have twenty-one solutions. Then discuss the solutions with them by having students identify any hexominoes that have not been used and tell why those hexominoes cannot be part of a solution.

Extension

Ask:

> *How many rectangles can you fill at the same time, without reusing any of the hexominoes?*

While some students will try to solve this problem at the concrete level by manipulating hexominoes, others will work at the representational level by studying the drawings in the solution set (their own tracings or the Answer Sheet on page 58).

Note: Some of the students who have explored septominoes independently may try to fill areas with them. They will find one that cannot be used unless the shape they are filling has a hole in it.

Exploring Hexominoes

Need: A copy of all the hexomino patterns, scissors, two copies of the puzzle sheet, an envelope

Answer Sheet for Exploring Hexominoes

EXPLORING WITH SQUARES AND CUBES
© Dale Seymour Publications

14. Designing and Evaluating Hexomino Puzzles (I)

Students will cut out squares and rectangles and test them to see if they can be filled in with hexominoes. Students will also learn about a method for determining if a solution is possible without actually finding one.

Student Materials: Several sheets of 1/2-inch grid paper
                     Scissors
                     Set of hexominoes
                     Activity Sheet on page 64

Getting Started

Begin by asking:

> *What is the largest possible area of a puzzle shape for hexominoes?*

Solicit ideas from students as to how to find the answer to this question. Eventually someone will suggest using the equation $6 \times 35 = 210$ (6 squares per hexomino × 35 hexominoes).

Exploring the Problem

Then ask:

> *How many squares and rectangles are there with areas that are multiples of 6 and between 0 and 210?*

Ask students to cut out several squares and rectangles with areas that are multiples of 6. Encourage them to cut out at least five or six such shapes before testing to see if they can be filled in with hexominoes. For some shapes, students may need to tape two pieces of grid paper together (as shown at right).

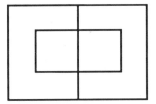

If none of the students cut out rectangles that have an area of 210 square units, work with the class to come up with the dimensions of several (for example, 14×15 or 7×30). Then have students explore the question of how many squares there are with areas that are multiples of 6 between 0 and 210. (There are only two: 6×6 and 12×12. See "Getting Started" in Exploration 7.)

Instruct students to select one of the squares or rectangles they have cut out and try to fill it in with hexominoes. If students find a way to fill their shapes with hexominoes, have them trace the solution and post it on the bulletin board. It may take students several attempts to solve some of the larger squares and rectangles. Solutions for the 6×6 and 12×12 squares are on the next page.

Challenge students to solve the rectangles that would require all thirty-five hexominoes (the ones with an area of 210). If students find some shapes impossible to solve, have them put those shapes aside for now. Other students may eventually want to take on the challenge of trying to find solutions for them.

One Solution for Each of the Two Possible Squares:

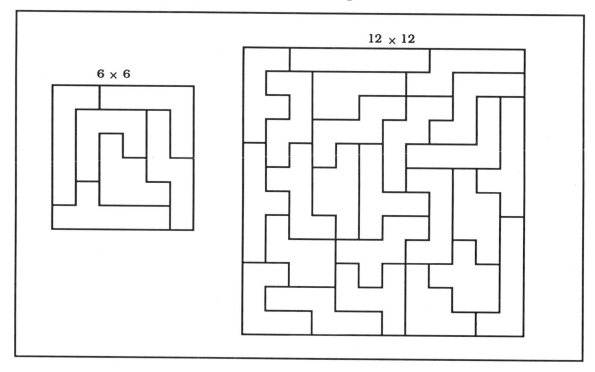

6 × 6

12 × 12

Follow-up

Encourage students to analyze the collection of all the squares and rectangles they have cut out in order to determine how many such shapes are possible. If necessary, remind them that organizing the data may make it easier to see if any squares or rectangles are missing from the group. (See "Exploring the Problem" in Exploration 7.)

Next post the squares and rectangles that have been declared impossible to solve. Ask students to describe any general characteristics or patterns they see. Encourage them to state why they think it is impossible to find solutions for some of the shapes. Sample responses are shown on the next page.

After allowing considerable time for student discussion, make this statement to the class:

All rectangles that have an area of 210 square units are impossible to fill in with hexominoes.

Then go through the following discussion with the class to explain the statement you have just made. Start by reading the paragraphs on the next page.

Almost a solution:

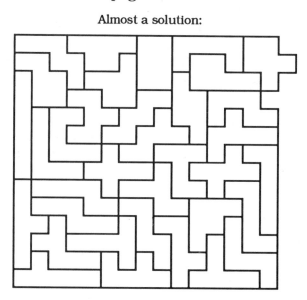

This is too long and too narrow.

This can be filled with duplicate pieces only.

All of these pieces have two- or four-square indentions, with the exception of six squares in a row. Anything longer will not be possible because the remaining pieces can only connect with pieces that have one- or three-square indentions.

two-square indention

three-square indention

Some things seem to be equivalent when they are not. Suppose two people each have six gloves. They both have the same number of gloves, but the sets of gloves are not necessarily equivalent. One person could have three left gloves and three right gloves and the other person could have four left gloves and two right gloves. (Notice that the first person has an uneven number of left and right gloves while the second person has an even number of each.)

Then suppose you had three people each with a right and left hand. Since you would have an uneven number of right and left hands, you could not put them into an even number of right and left gloves (as held by the second person described above). These three people could only fit their uneven number of right and left hands into an uneven number of gloves (as held by the first person described above).

Just because you have six gloves doesn't mean three people can wear them. The same is true for the arrangements of squares you have been working with.

Distribute the Activity Sheet on page 64. The top part of this page has a rectangle with an area that is equal to the sum of all the areas of the five arrangements of four squares shown at the bottom of the page. (These five arrangements are all the possible arrangements of four squares.)

Instruct students to color in every other square of the rectangle so that it looks like a checkerboard. Then ask:

How many squares did you fill in? (10)

Point out to students that there are ten white squares and ten colored squares, an *even* number of each. Then have them color in every other square in each of the five arrangements at the bottom of the page. Ask:

How many squares did you fill in? (9 or 11)

The answer can be either 9 or 11 depending on how students filled in this shape:

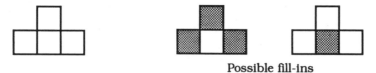

Possible fill-ins

Now point out to students that whether they have nine white squares and eleven colored squares, or eleven white squares and nine colored squares, either way they have an *uneven* number of each. Remind students that they cannot cover an even number of things with an uneven number of things.

Encourage students to test this result by cutting out the five arrangements of four squares and trying to use them to fill in the 4 × 5 rectangle.

Then have students use the checkerboard method to evaluate the statement that hexominoes cannot be used to fill in any rectangle that has 210 square units. (You may want to provide students with another copy of the hexomino patterns on pages 52 and 53. Or you could use just one set to demonstrate the results to the class.)

When all the hexominoes have been colored in, have students sort the arrangements according to whether they have an even or uneven number of colored and white squares. You may find it helpful to use a chart like the one shown here. In the end students will see that twenty-four hexominoes have an uneven number of white squares and colored squares and eleven hexominoes have an even number of each. (See the solution on page 65).

Number of white and colored squares	
Uneven	Even

By using multiplication and addition, you can see that there are an even number of colored squares and an even number of white squares. Any rectangle with an area of 210 square units, however, will always have an *uneven* number of colored squares and white squares. Therefore, the thirty-five hexominoes cannot be used to completely cover any rectangle with an area of 210 square units.

Independent Exploration

☐ ☐ ☐ ☐ ☐ ☐

Students could work on the first part of this exploration independently by following the procedures described on Labsheet 14. Given the large number of possible squares and rectangles for students to work with, you may find it most beneficial for them to work in small groups. Encourage groups to evaluate their collection of squares and rectangles and to discuss why some rectangles may be impossible to solve. Be sure all students have an opportunity to take part in the discussion of the checkerboard method of determining whether or not a rectangle can have a hexomino solution.

Designing and Evaluating Hexomino Puzzles (I)

Need: 1/2-inch grid paper, scissors, set of hexominoes

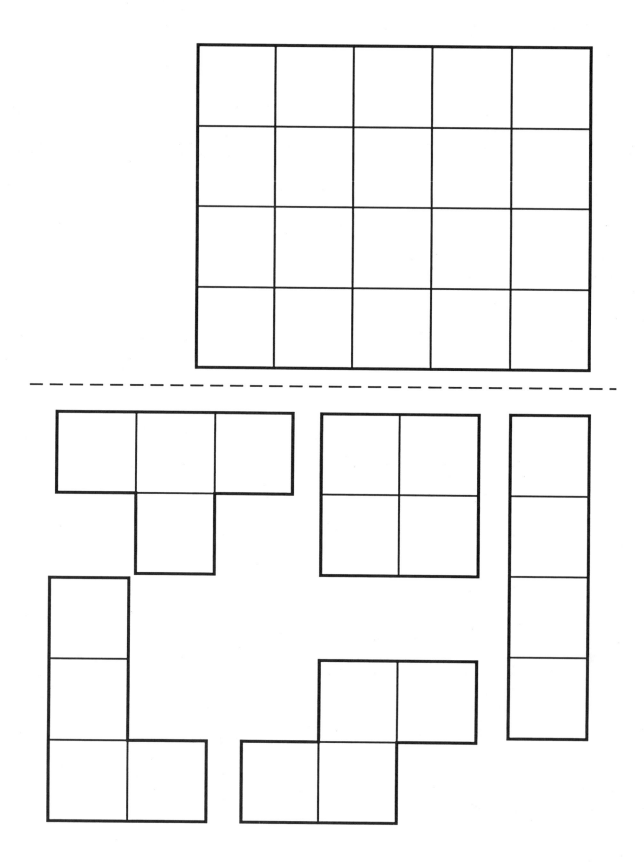

Diagram of Checkerboard Hexominoes and Related Rectangle

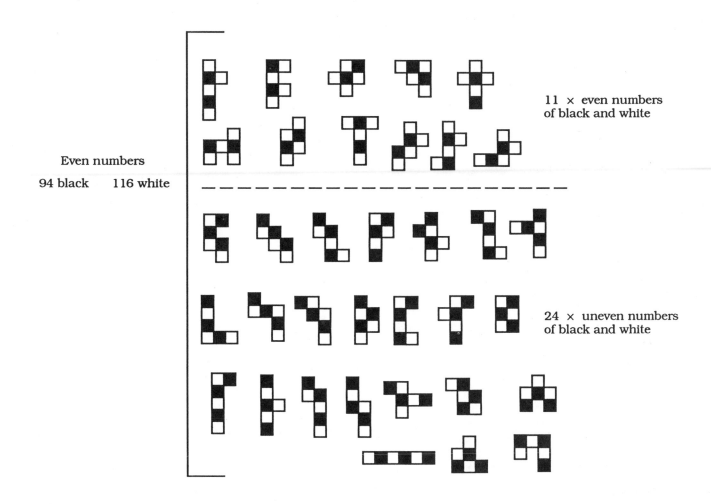

Even numbers

94 black   116 white

11 × even numbers of black and white

24 × uneven numbers of black and white

Uneven numbers

105 black   105 white

From *Polyominoes* by Solomon Golomb. New York: Scribner, 1965, pp.28–29.

15. Designing and Evaluating Hexomino Puzzles (II)

Students will design hexomino puzzle shapes that either are symmetrical or are squares or rectangles with holes or notches in them. Then students will determine which shapes are possible to fill in with hexominoes and try to find solutions for them.

Student Materials: Several sheets of 1/2-inch grid paper

                       Set of hexominoes

                       Puzzle Pattern on page 69 (optional)

Getting Started

Review the concept of symmetry with students. Remind them that a shape is symmetrical if you can draw a line through the center of it and have both halves look the same.

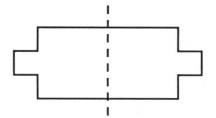

Exploring the Problem

Have students recall how they used grid paper to make pentomino puzzles in Exploration 9. Explain that they will now use the same procedures to make hexomino puzzles. If necessary, remind students that the shapes must have areas that are multiples of 6. Encourage students to make the shapes symmetrical. Encourage them also to make some shapes that are squares or rectangles with holes or notches in them. Allow time for students to make several shapes and then test them.

If students find shapes that cannot be filled in with hexominoes, encourage them to find out why (see Exploration 14), modify the shapes, and test them again. The range of possible shapes and sizes is suggested by the drawings shown here.

Provide an opportunity for students to solve each other's puzzles. Students can either trade puzzles among themselves or post them on the bulletin board so that students can look them over and decide which ones they want to solve. Or, you could collect the shapes and make a puzzle book.

For the second part of this exploration, challenge students to make a symmetrical shape, or a square or rectangle with a hole or notches, that has an area of 210 square units. Allow students ample time to discover several such shapes.

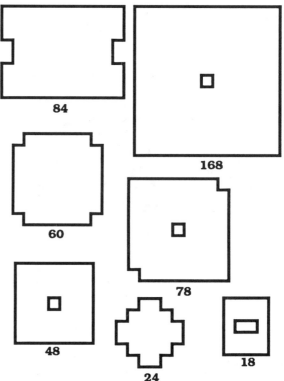

66

Then ask each student to choose one shape and use the checkerboard method to determine whether or not it can be filled in with hexominoes. (If necessary, review the checkerboard method as explained in Exploration 14.) If students discover shapes that will not have solutions, encourage them to modify the shapes and try again.

Once students have found shapes for which solutions are possible, encourage them to try to find solutions. Note that finding solutions for areas that require all thirty-five hexominoes can be very difficult. Some students may want to take the puzzles home to work on them. (Remind students to bring the hexominoes back to class so that they will have them for future explorations.)

You may want to create two posting areas for the puzzles with 210 square units—one for shapes that have been proved possible but have not yet been solved and the other for shapes that have been solved. Then students can select puzzles from the first area to work on as they have time. Once a student has found a solution, it can be posted in the solutions area.

Follow-up

The puzzle pattern on page 69 is the smallest possible square (with a hole) that can be filled in with all thirty-five hexominoes. If students have not created this shape on their own, distribute copies of page 69 and ask students to try to find a solution.

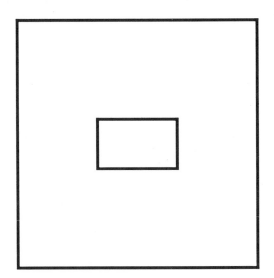

Solution:

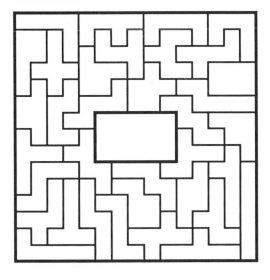

Independent Exploration

☐ ☐ ☐ ☐ ☐ ☐

If you want to have students work more independently, distribute copies of Labsheet 15. Encourage students to read the instructions carefully. This activity will work best if students work in pairs or small groups so that they can trade puzzles and work together to figure out which shapes will be impossible to solve.

Designing and Evaluating Hexomino Puzzles (II)

Need: Five sheets of 1/2-inch grid paper, set of hexominoes

A Use the grid paper to draw shapes that could be filled in with hexominoes.

The shapes must have areas that are multiples of 6.

Try to make the shapes symmetrical. . .

. . . or squares and rectangles with holes and notches in them.

Try to fill in one of your shapes with hexominoes.

Trade shapes with someone else. Try to solve each other's puzzle.

Color in the area like a checkerboard and count the number of colored squares and white squares.

If the area has an even number of colored squares and white squares, it is possible to fill it in with hexominoes.

B Use grid paper to make a symmetrical shape—or a rectangle or square with a hole or notch in it—that has an area of 210 square units.

210 square units equals the total area of all 35 hexominoes.

If your shape is too large, you may need to tape two pieces of grid paper together.

Try to fill in your shape with hexominoes. Trace the solution and post it.

If your shape is impossible to fill in with hexominoes, modify it and try again.

Puzzle Pattern for the Smallest Possible Square
(with a hole)

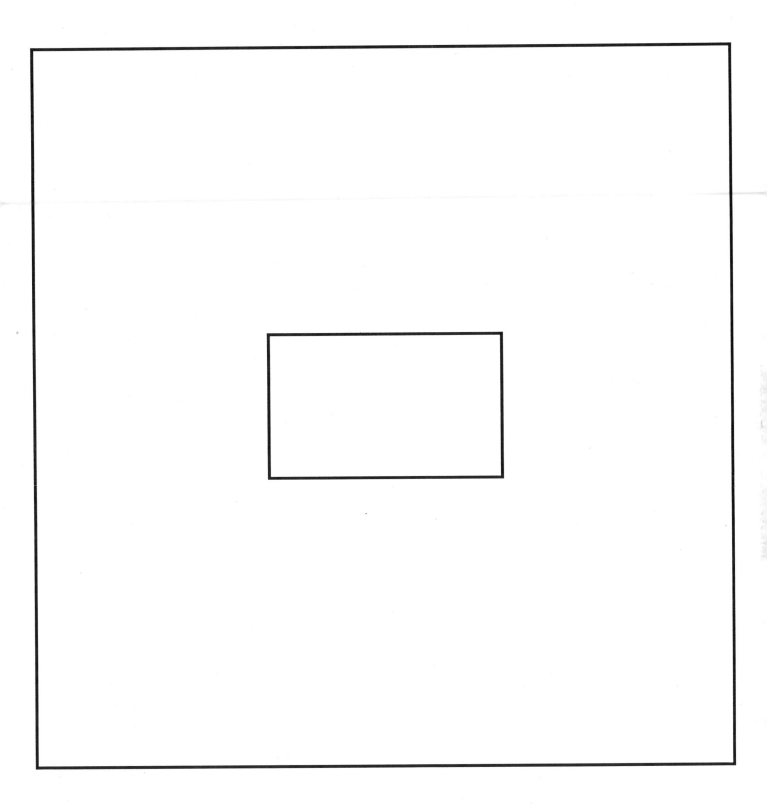

16. "Hexiosaurs" (an optional science application) □ □ □ □ □ □

Students will use hexominoes to create dinosaur shapes. They will also create dinosaur shapes based on a grid and try to fill them in with hexominoes.

Teacher Materials: Demonstration hexominoes:

Student Materials: Several sheets of 1/2-inch grid paper
Set of hexominoes

Getting Started

To stir up students' imagination and set the mood for synthesis and trans- formation, ask them to name several kinds of dinosaurs. Write the names on the chalkboard or on chart paper. This list will help students bring to mind a variety of dinosaur shapes.

Stegosaurus
Apatosaur
Tyrannosaur
Triceratops
Plateosaur

Exploring the Problem

Hold up these hexominoes:

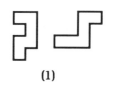

(1)

Then combine them like (2) and hold them against the chalkboard. Trace around the outline of the shape, remove the hexominoes, and reveal the dinosaur shape to students (3).

Challenge students to use hexominoes to create dinosaur shapes of their own. Tell students these shapes are called "hexiosaurs."

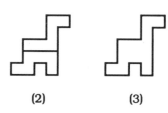

(2)   (3)

Encourage students to create several hexiosaurs by tracing around hexominoes positioned on their grid paper. This usually results in students creating several small dinosaur shapes.

The second part of this exploration is the inverse of the first. For this part of the activity, instruct students to draw dinosaur shapes on the grid paper without first putting down the hexominoes. This usually results in larger shapes than the first method. Remind students that the hexiosaurs they draw need to have areas that are multiples of 6. After students have tested their shapes, and modified them if necessary, they may want to trade with other students and try to solve each other's puzzles.

Example hexiosaurs are shown on page 73.

Follow-up

Among the hexiosaurs that students draw in the second part of this activity, there may be several that will be impossible to fill in with hexominoes. Ask students to examine those shapes and explain why they are impossible to solve. If a hexiosaur has a long neck or legs, for example, there might not be enough narrow hexominoes to fill in the space (see "Follow-up" in Exploration 14).

If students have created any dinosaur shapes that have an area of 210 square units, have them use the checkerboard method to see if it is possible to fill in the shapes with hexominoes (see Exploration 14). A hexiosaur of this size would need to have an even number of both colored and white squares in order to have a hexomino solution. Even then it might not be possible due to other reasons.

Collect students' hexiosaurs, make copies of their outlines, and distribute the shapes (singly or stapled together in a book) for students to solve with their hexominoes. When students have found a solution, have them make a record of it by tracing the hexominoes they have used.

Independent Exploration

Students can complete this activity on their own by following the procedures described on Labsheet 16. Have students work in pairs or small groups so that they will be able to trade puzzles. If students create any hexiosaurs that are impossible to solve, help them find out how they could modify the shapes so that they will have solutions.

"Hexiosaurs"

Need: Set of hexominoes

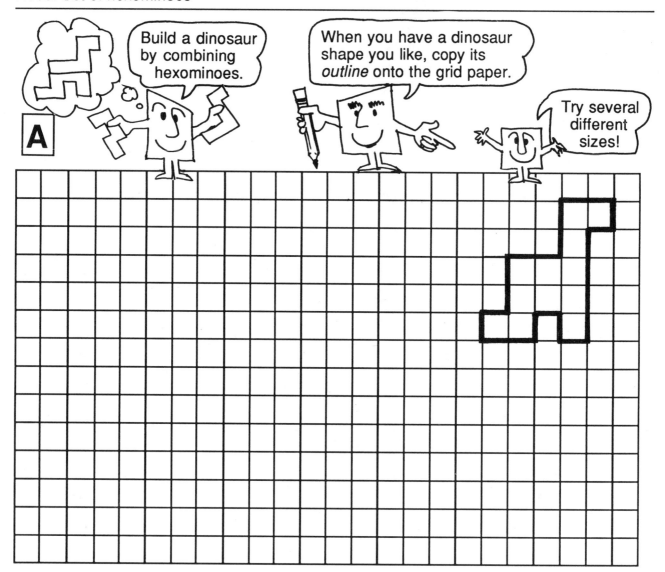

Need: Several sheets of 1/2-inch grid paper, set of hexominoes

EXPLORING WITH SQUARES AND CUBES
© Dale Seymour Publications

Examples of Hexiosaurs

17. Sorting Hexominoes by Perimeter □ □ □ □ □ □

Students will sort regular hexominoes according to perimeter and then look for patterns in the collected data.

Teacher Materials: Demonstration hexominoes, with double-sided tape on the back of each one
Butcher paper

Student Materials: Two sheets of 1-inch grid paper (Square Grid 4, page 152)
Scissors
Double-sided tape or glue

Getting Started

Press the two demonstration hexominoes onto the chalk-board. Then show how to find the perimeter of each one by tracing around its outline with chalk:

After determining the perimeter of these hexominoes, ask students to decide the area of each one. Then ask:

How can two shapes with the same area have different perimeters?

Draw this chart on butcher paper and post it where all students can see it from their desks. Then post the two demonstration hexominoes in the correct columns of the chart.

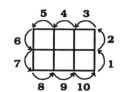

Perimeter				
10	11	12	13	14

Exploring the Problem

Ask students to cut several hexominoes out of their grid paper. Then have them find the perimeter of each one and post on the chart using double-sided tape or glue. (Double-sided tape is easier to use because it allows students to remove duplicates or errors from the chart.)

Follow-up

When students have completed the chart, encourage them to look for patterns in the organized data. (You may wish to give students a copy of the completed chart on page 76 so that they can examine it closely and write on it as needed.) Encourage students to evaluate the patterns others have identified by testing their validity against the chart. Example patterns are shown on the next page.

Example Patterns:

1. There are no odd-numbered perimeters.

2. All hexominoes with perimeter 12 include a large square made up of four small squares.

3. All hexominoes with perimeter 12 include a rectangle made up of three squares.

4. All hexominoes with perimeter 14 include a rectangle made up of two squares.

5. None of the hexominoes with perimeter 14 include a large square made up of four small squares.

Students will undoubtedly find variations in these patterns as they examine the data. Accept any patterns they find as long as they can justify them using data from the chart.

For patterns 2, 3, and 4 above, students identify embedded shapes in the hexominoes. (This will help prepare them for later activities.) Encourage them to look at the hexominoes with perimeter 14 and suggest embedded shapes that are *not* found in all of them. Students may want to sort the hexominoes in that column into subcategories according to whether they include embedded shapes such as (1) and (2).

Perimeter Chart

18. Grouping Hexominoes by Embedded Components

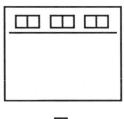

Students will create hexominoes by combining two or three groups of squares in different ways.

Teacher Materials: Three pairs of 4-inch squares
cut out of orange construction
paper, with double-sided tape
on the back of each one

One sheet of 1-inch grid paper

Chart paper

Scissors

Double-sided tape

Student Materials: Several sheets of 1-inch grid paper

Scissors

Double-sided tape or glue

Getting Started

Create a chart by drawing three pairs of squares at the top of the chart paper. Then post the chart where all students can see it from their desks. Ask:

How many hexominoes can you make by combining three pairs of squares?

Demonstrate how to make a hexomino with the three pairs by pressing them on the chalkboard in this arrangement:

Then outline the shape with chalk and remove the three pairs of squares. Cut this shape out of 1-inch grid paper and post it on the chart.

Exploring the Problem

Part 1

Have students cut out three pairs of 1-inch squares from their grid paper. Then ask students to combine the three pairs in different ways to create as many different hexominoes as possible. Each time students create a hexomino shape, have them copy the shape onto the grid paper and cut it out.

After all students have cut out at least ten hexominoes, invite them to post their solutions on the chart with double-sided tape or glue. Caution students to look for duplicates before adding their hexominoes to the ones already there. Save a set of duplicates for the Follow-up and leave the chart up for the next part of this activity. The solution set is shown on the next page.

Solution Set:

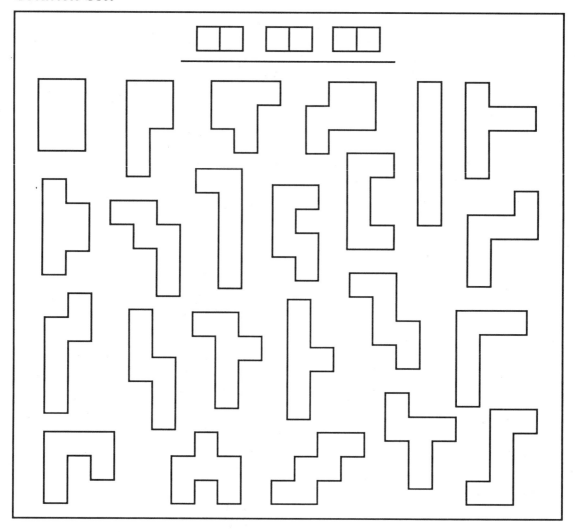

Part 2

Create charts like the ones shown below and post them around the classroom:

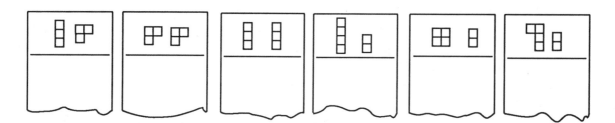

Instruct students to each choose one of the charts and cut out of their grid paper the two shapes pictured at the top. Then have students combine the two shapes in different ways to create several different hexominoes. Students can then copy their hexominoes on the grid paper, cut them out, and post them on the chart. Encourage students to contribute to as many charts as they can.

Solution Set:

Follow-up

Have students carefully examine each of the charts from Part 2 to see if it is complete. If they decide that a chart is not complete, have them identify the missing hexominoes, cut them out of grid paper, and post them on the chart. Also have students check to see that all the hexominoes on a chart can indeed be formed from the two shapes shown at the top of the chart. Instruct students to remove any incorrect hexominoes as well as any duplicates.

Place double-sided tape on the back of the duplicate hexominoes you saved from Part 1. Press them to the chalkboard in rows with space below. Then have students help you make a frequency table by putting tally marks below each hexomino to show how many charts it was posted on in Parts 1 and 2. (See page 81 for a completed frequency table.)

Ask students to examine the frequency table and describe any patterns they see. Examples:

1. The rectangle with the smallest perimeter appears most often.
2. All the hexominoes that do not "branch" appear at least three times (except for one).
3. The cross does not appear on any chart.

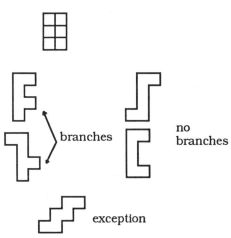

79

Discuss the third pattern by asking:

How can you divide the cross into two pieces?

Ask students to cut out these two shapes and use them to create several hexominoes. Draw, or have students draw, the hexominoes they find on the chalkboard.

Solution Set:

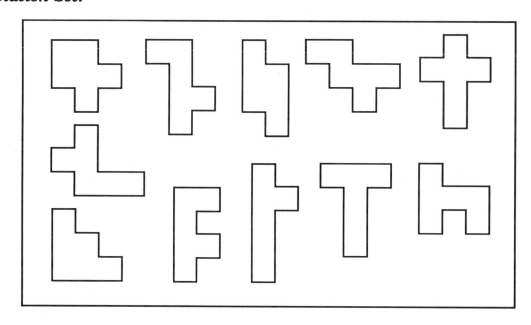

Then ask:

How are most of these hexominoes alike?

Students will probably notice that most of these hexominoes have a very low frequency, usually appearing only once on the charts.

Note: Students who take this exploration to the level of independent investigation may want to create additional charts such as these:

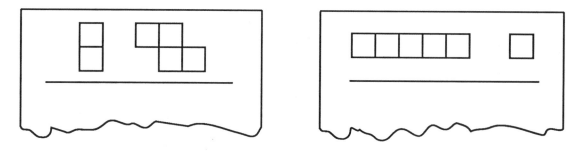

They may want to add their charts to the frequency table and see what affect it has on the three patterns described on page 79. In addition, students who have been exploring septominoes independently may want to display their charts and share their conclusions. (If you have more than one or two "septominoists" in your class, ask them to start a "Septomino Club.")

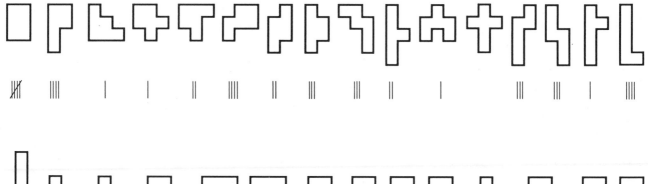

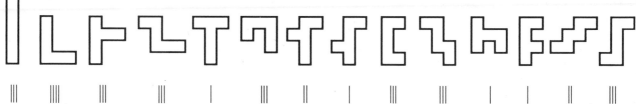

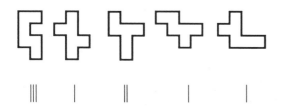

19. Exploring Hexomic Roots □ □ □ □ □ □

Students will sort hexominoes according to which pentominoes they could be made of.

Teacher Materials: Set of twelve pentominoes saved from Exploration 4

Set of thirty-five hexominoes saved from Exploration 12

Getting Started

Use the twelve pentominoes from Exploration 3 to set up a chart of hexomic roots on a large bulletin board.

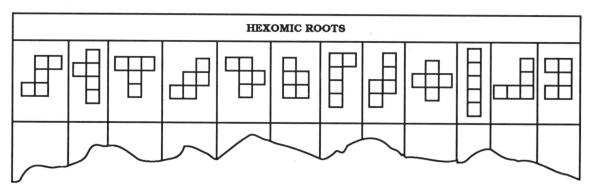

Post the thirty-five hexominoes from Exploration 12 on another bulletin board so that students can reach them easily.

Point out to students that every hexomino can be made by adding one square to a pentomino. Hold up one of the hexominoes from the ones posted on the bulletin board and ask:

Which pentomino could have been used to make this hexomino?

Post the hexomino under the appropriate pentomino on the chart. If there are two or more appropriate pentominoes, post the hexomino under any one of them. (The hexomino [1], for example, could be posted under either [2] or [3].)

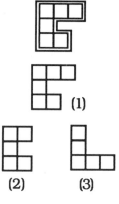

Exploring the Problem

Invite students to take turns choosing one of the hexominoes and posting it in an appropriate column of the chart. As students post the hexominoes, ask other students to confirm that they have been posted correctly. If a student finds an error, allow that student to move the hexomino to a different column.

If some columns are still empty after all the hexominoes have been posted, invite students to move some of the hexominoes so that every column has at least one member.

Follow-up

Discuss the chart with students. Ask:

Is it possible to sort the hexominoes so that all of the columns have the same number of hexominoes?

Give students time to answer. If necessary, point out that it is not possible because there are an odd number of hexominoes and an even number of pentominoes. Ask:

What would be the best sorting arrangement to have nearly equal columns?

Give students time to answer by dividing the number of hexominoes by the number of columns in the chart (35 ÷ 12). Students will see that the best arrangement would be to have eleven columns with three hexominoes and one column with two hexominoes. Then ask:

Is it possible to sort the hexominoes so that there are no more than three in a column?

Give students several opportunities to rearrange the hexominoes on the chart, switching them from one column to another, so that the columns have nearly equal numbers of hexominoes. Encourage students to continue evaluating how the hexominoes have been posted. (For the solution set, see the dark figures in the top part of the Hexomic Roots chart on page 88.)

Note: Save this completed chart for use in Exploration 20.

20. Exploring Multiple Roots of Hexominoes □ □ □ □ □ □

Students will find all the pentomino roots of the thirty-five hexominoes. They will also analyze the pentominoes for line and point symmetry and use the results to explore the chart of Hexomic Roots.

Note: This activity is an extension of Exploration 19. It is a long activity and should be spread over several days, or even a week.

Teacher Materials: The chart of hexomic roots from Exploration 19

A demonstration hexomino
made from 1-inch grid paper

A large demonstration pentomino

Butcher paper

Student Materials: Several sheets of 1-inch grid paper

Pentomino patterns on pages 15 and 16

Scissors

Getting Started

Review the chart of hexomic roots and remind students that they found that most of the hexominoes could go in more than one of the columns. Post the demonstration hexomino on the chart in whichever of the two columns where it isn't already posted. Point out to students that the chart now contains duplicate hexominoes (that are like the demonstration hexomino).

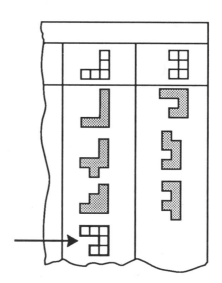

Exploring the Problem

Part 1

Ask students to cut several hexominoes out of their grid paper. Invite students to post their hexominoes on the chart in columns that don't have those shapes already. Have students post the hexominoes below the ones already posted as part of Exploration 19. Challenge students to find a hexomino that can be posted in three different columns of the chart. Can they find one that can be posted in four different columns?

Have students continue posting the duplicate hexominoes with multiple roots until the class is satisfied that the chart is complete. During the posting time, encourage students to evaluate each other's choices to be sure that no hexominoes have been posted incorrectly. The complete solution set is shown on page 88.

Part 2

Draw this chart on butcher paper and post it in the classroom:

Symmetry of Pentominoes					
Asymmetrical	Symmetrical				
		Line			Point
		1	2	4	

Hold up the demonstration pentomino and fold it in half crosswise. Then reopen the pentomino and draw a line along the fold. Remind the class that a shape is symmetrical if you can draw a line through the middle of it and have both halves look the same. Explain that the line drawn along the fold is called a *line of symmetry*. Ask students if they can suggest another line of symmetry for this pentomino. Someone will probably suggest folding the pentomino lengthwise. Fold the pentomino lengthwise, reopen it, and mark the new line of symmetry. Announce to students that this pentomino has two lines of symmetry.

Then demonstrate to students that this pentomino also has *point symmetry*. Push a straight pin through the intersection of the two lines of symmetry and rotate the shape 180°. Emphasize that since the pentomino looks the same when rotated around a point, it is said to have point symmetry. (Students should understand that full turns of 360° are not allowed in demonstrating point symmetry.)

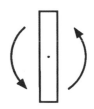

Ask students to cut out the pentomino patterns and test each one for line and point symmetry. After allowing time for students to work with the pentominoes, invite them to share their results with the class. Encourage them to post the pentominoes in the correct columns of the chart on the bulletin board.

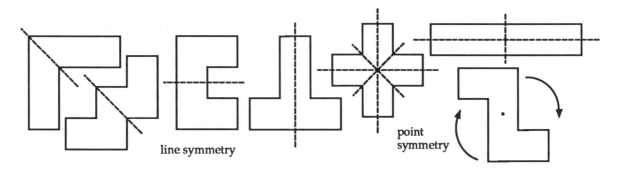

line symmetry

point symmetry

Some pentominoes will have both line and point symmetry. Have students post these pentominoes in both columns. If necessary, explain to students that pentominoes with neither line nor point symmetry are *asymmetrical*. There will be five such pentominoes. Have students post these on the chart in the appropriate columns.

Completed Chart:

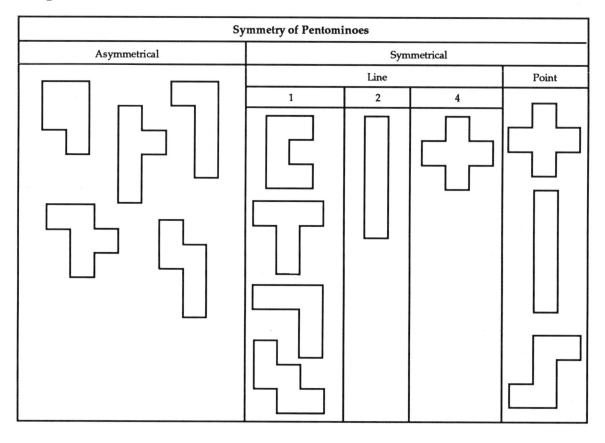

Follow-up

Instruct students to study and compare the "Symmetry of Pentominoes" and "Hexomic Roots" charts. Ask:

What patterns do you see in the chart of Hexomic Roots?

Invite students to describe any patterns they see. Some students may also want to make some specific observations, such as the fact that hexominoes 1–4 each fit in one column only. Hexomino 5, on the other hand, fits in four columns.

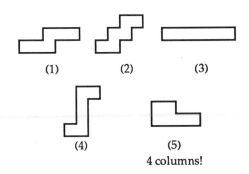

(1)   (2)   (3)

(4)   (5)
4 columns!

Example Patterns for Both Charts:

1. The asymmetrical pentominoes have the longest columns of resulting hexominoes.
2. The pentomino with the most lines of symmetry has the shortest column of hexominoes.
3. The pentomino with the second most lines of symmetry has the second shortest column.
4. In general, then, the more lines of symmetry a pentomino has, the fewer hexominoes that can be formed from it.

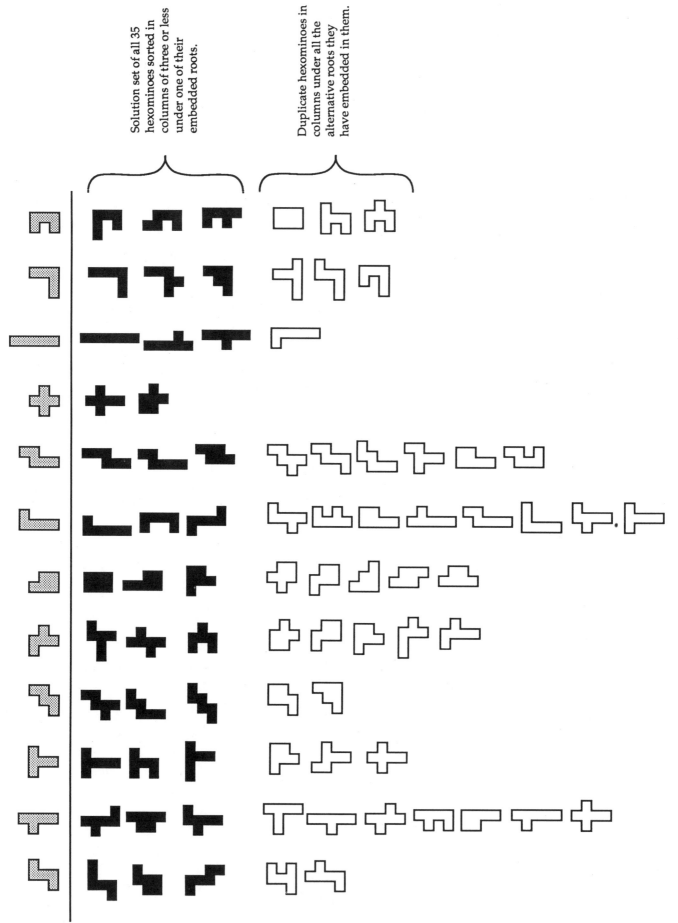

Solution set of all 35 hexominoes sorted in columns of three or less under one of their embedded roots.

Duplicate hexominoes in columns under all the alternative roots they have embedded in them.

21. Sequencing Hexominoes

Students will create sequences of hexominoes in which each hexomino can be made by moving one square in the preceding hexomino one square's distance.

Teacher Materials:　Demonstration hexominoes:

Student Materials:　Set of hexominoes
　　　　　　　　　　Several 4" × 18" strips of manila paper

Getting Started

Review the concept of sequencing. Remind students that sequencing is a way of ordering the members of a set according to a particular rule. Letters, for example, can be alphabetized, and numbers can be put in counting order according to the rule $n + 1$.

Exploring the Problem

If you feel it is necessary to review how to sequence pentominoes or hexominoes, remind students of the rule:

Move one square one square's distance.

Then hold up the three demonstration hexominoes and help students arrange them in a sequence. Start by posting the rectangular hexomino. Ask:

If you moved the middle square on the right down one square diagonally, which of the other two hexominoes would it look like?

After someone chooses the second demonstration hexomino, post it to the right of the first hexomino and put an arrow between the two.

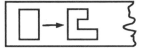

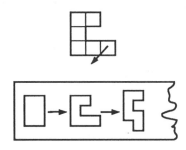

Next ask students what would happen if you moved the last square on the bottom right of the second hexomino down one square diagonally. Hold up the third demonstration hexomino and post it on the bulletin board in sequence after the other two. Add an arrow between the second and third hexominoes.

Ask students to choose one of the columns on the "Hexomic Roots" chart, take the same hexominoes shown there from their own sets of hexominoes, and put those hexominoes in order according to the sequencing rule. Students may need to rearrange the hexominoes several times before they are able to find a sequence. Instruct students to trace the sequences they do find on the strips of manila paper. Remind them to draw arrows to show the sequence.

Then have groups of students work together to create longer sequences by combining the ones they have made individually. Point out that they may need to reverse or rearrange their sequences in order to match the beginning of another person's sequence. Remind them also to be on the lookout for duplicates.

Encourage students to try linear sequences first, but if they reach a stalemate, remind them that they can also work with branching sequences (see Exploration 10). In this exploration, it will be easy for students to add the "branches." Students can tack a sequence strip on to the first one so that it is perpendicular.

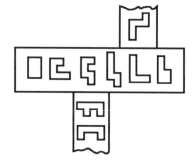

Be sure all students have an opportunity to work with others. Post many examples of partial sequences on the bulletin board. Then students may see how they can connect their partial sequences with what has already been posted. Challenge groups of students to create one long sequence that includes *all thirty-five* hexominoes.

Follow-up

Show several of the sequences completed by students and have the class evaluate them according to the sequencing rule. If students were unable to find one long sequence for all thirty-five hexominoes, explore that problem now as a whole class activity. Use partial sequences that students have already created, or start again from scratch.

Example Sequence Fragments:

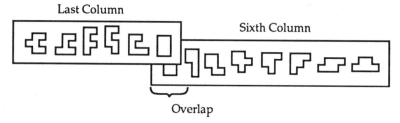

This might be a good time to remind students of how they have been acting like scientists. Bring out the behavioral verbs collected during the "Setting the Stage" discussion outlined on page *xii*. Invite students to choose a few appropriate verbs. Examples: experimenting, organizing, sequencing, revising, comparing, analyzing, etc.

Note: If you have any independent "septominoists" who have been sequencing their shapes, have them show some of their results to the class.

Independent Exploration

Students can work on this activity independently by following the instructions outlined on Labsheet 21. Encourage students to work in small groups so that they can combine their partial sequences. Then you can have groups exchange the longer sequences so that they can evaluate them according to the sequencing rule. Conclude the activity by discussing the behavioral verbs with the class.

Sequencing Hexominoes

Need: Set of hexominoes, several 4" x 18" strips of manila paper

22. Folding Hexominoes into Cubes ☐ ☐ ☐ ☐ ☐ ☐

Students will determine which of the hexominoes can be folded into cubes and which can be folded into cups.

Teacher Materials: A small box like the kind in which gift coffee mugs are packaged (Look through the supermarket. Boxes of tea bags are good. Try to find a box as cubical as possible.)
Butcher paper
Double-sided tape

Student Materials: Several sheets of 1-inch grid paper
Scissors

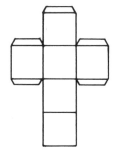

Getting Started

Hold up the box in front of the class. Then take the box apart and flatten it out. Ask students which hexomino the flattened box most closely resembles.

Will it fold into a cube?	
Yes	No

Exploring the Problem

Draw this chart on butcher paper and post it in the classroom. Then ask:

Which of the hexominoes can be folded into a cube?

Instruct students to cut several hexominoes out of their grid paper. Then have them try to fold each one to see if it can be made into a complete cube. Encourage them to cut and fold carefully. Tell students to create two piles of hexominoes on their desks: YES it will make a cube, and NO it will not make a cube. Remind students to save all their attempts. The failures are as important as the successes. (Ask any scientist!)

When students have cut, tested, and sorted at least ten hexominoes, have them study the hexominoes in each pile to see how they are alike. Some students may want to test all thirty-five hexominoes before comparing them. Other students may only want to test several.

Invite students to post their hexominoes on the chart. Encourage other students to make sure that each hexomino has been placed in the correct column. When students have completed the chart, ask students to generalize a rule or description for at least three of the hexominoes in either column. Again, encourage students to evaluate each other's statements by applying them to the chart.

Example Responses:

Yes column Some of the hexominoes in this column have four squares in a row with one square "sticking out" on each side.

No column Some of the hexominoes in this column have four squares that are arranged in a larger square.

Other hexominoes in this column have four squares in a row with two squares both "sticking out" on the same side.

Follow-up

Discuss the results of this exploration with students. Ask:

How may ways are there to design a pattern that can be used to build a box? (The chart should show eleven ways.)

Application

Ask students which box pattern they think is used most frequently in industry. Remind them of the box you showed them in the introduction. Point out that the cross-shaped pattern is easy to assemble by automatic machines. Demonstrate with a hexomino how the pattern is folded:

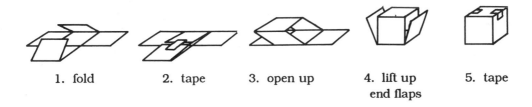

| 1. fold | 2. tape | 3. open up | 4. lift up end flaps | 5. tape |

Some students might have observed during the earlier exploration that some of the hexominoes that didn't quite form cubes could be made into cups. (A cup is like a cube with one side open and one side overlapped.)

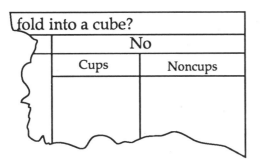

Remove all the hexominoes from the No column of the chart. Then divide that column into two subcolumns as shown.

Next have students test all the hexominoes just removed from the chart to see which can be folded into cups. Have students repost the hexominoes in the appropriate subcolumns. Then have students generalize a rule or description for at least three of the hexominoes that can be folded into a cup.

93

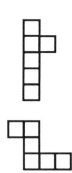

Some of the hexominoes that can be folded into a cup have five squares in a row with one square "sticking out."

Some of the other hexominoes that can be folded into a cup have three squares in a row with one square "sticking out" on one side and two squares "sticking out" on the other.

Completed Chart for Cups and Noncups:

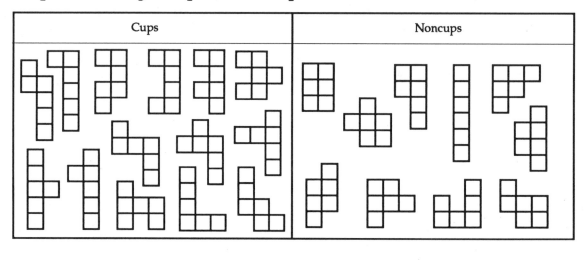

Cups	Noncups

Independent Exploration

If you want to have students work more independently, distribute Labsheet 22. Encourage students to read and follow the instructions carefully. Once students have tested and sorted at least ten hexominoes, and had a chance to see how the hexominoes in each group are alike, encourage them to come up with generalizations for the shapes in each group. Then work with students to determine which of the nonbox shapes can be made into cups.

Note: At this point, students who have been exploring the septominoes may want to try sorting them by folding. Possible categories are suggested below.

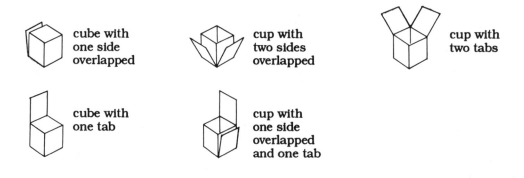

cube with one side overlapped

cup with two sides overlapped

cup with two tabs

cube with one tab

cup with one side overlapped and one tab

Folding Hexominoes into Cubes

Need: Several sheets of 1-inch grid paper, scissors

Solution for Chart

Will it fold into a cube?

Yes	No

EXPLORING WITH SQUARES AND CUBES
© Dale Seymour Publications

23. Exploring Arrangements of Four Cubes ▫▫▫▫

Students will recreate the Soma puzzle, which was discovered by Pat Heim using the same process students will use here.

Teacher Materials:　Eight 1-inch (or larger) cubes

　　　　　　　　　Masking tape

　　　　　　　　　Demonstration models of the solution set on page 98
　　　　　　　　　　(made of the same size cubes as the eight cubes above)

Student Materials:　Four wooden 1-inch cubes

　　　　　　　　　Masking tape

Getting Started

Hold up three cubes and ask:

How many ways can you arrange three cubes?

If students need help getting started, demonstrate one way to arrange three cubes.

Point out that the faces of the cubes that are touching must match up. Then demonstrate an arrangement of cubes that does not meet this condition.

It will take students only a few minutes to realize that there are only two ways to arrange three cubes. Make a model of each solution by taping three cubes together.

At this point in the discussion, you might also want to demonstrate that there is only one way to arrange two cubes.

Hold up the two arrangements of three cubes. Ask:

Which of these arrangements of three cubes is regular? Which is irregular?

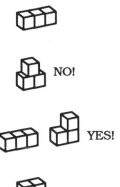
NO!
YES!

If you need to review the meaning of the term *regular*, point out to students that boxes of dry food in the supermarket are examples of *regular* rectangular prisms. Then have students identify each of the two arrangements as regular or irregular.

 regular　　　 irregular

You should save the model of the irregular arrangement for use during the Follow-up discussion, but you can take the regular arrangement apart.

Exploring the Problem

Ask:

How many irregular arrangements of four cubes can you find?

Give four cubes to each student and allow sufficient time for them to explore several arrangements. Then have each student use masking tape to tape together one of the arrangements they have found. Make sure students align the cubes carefully so that the faces match up as exactly as possible. Remind students to use small pieces of tape.

Invite students to bring taped arrangements to the front of the room. If you feel the need for students to remain seated, walk around the class and collect completed arrangements. (Include some duplicates in the collection for students to discover during evaluation.)

Then evaluate the taped arrangements. Ask:

Does each arrangement have four cubes?
Do the faces of the cubes match up?
Is each arrangement irregular?
Are there any duplicates?

After students have eliminated all the duplicates, ask if there are any arrangements missing. Give an additional four cubes to any students who believe they have a new arrangement. Evaluate new arrangements. When all the solutions have been found, announce:

There are six and only six irregular arrangements of four cubes.

Note: Have students save their arrangements for use in Exploration 24.

Solution Set:

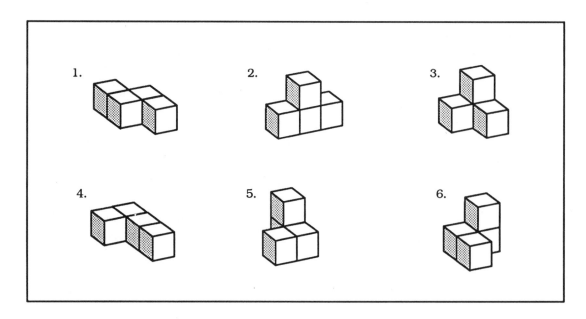

Note: Either arrangement 5 or arrangement 6 is usually the last to be discovered because these arrangements are the mirror images of each other. If some students think that these two solutions are exactly the same, have them pick up one of the models and try to flip it or turn it so that it looks exactly like the other. It can't be done. One arrangement is left-handed and the other is right-handed. Students may be interested to know that scientists have noticed that in nature atomic particles are either right-handed or left-handed and that the right-handed forms of some nonlethal drugs are deadly.

Some students might point out that mirror images were not considered new solutions for pentominoes and hexominoes. Explain that while you can flip a two-dimensional shape over so that it looks exactly like its mirror image, you cannot do the same thing with a three-dimensional shape.

Follow-up

Soma puzzle

Tell students that all the irregular arrangements of three and four cubes can be stacked into a larger cube with dimensions $3 \times 3 \times 3$. Show that this is possible by having students confirm that $6 \times 4 + 3 = 3 \times 3 \times 3$. Then proceed to stack the seven models into a large cube. (Rehearse solving the cube several times before class so that you can surprise the class with a quick solution.)

One of Many Solutions:

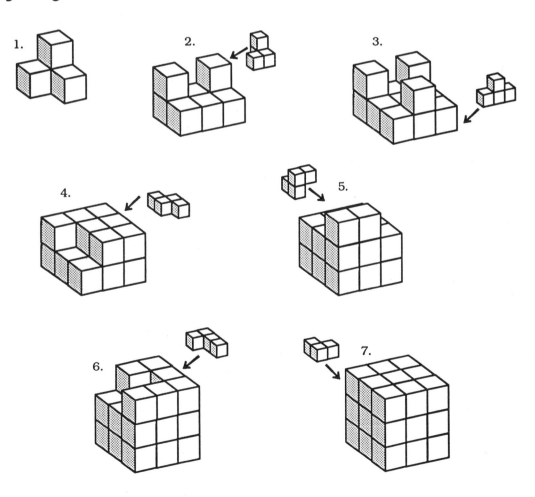

Then allow time for students to create $3 \times 3 \times 3$ cubes with the seven irregular arrangements. Students can use the arrangements of wooden cubes that they have taped together (or sugar cubes, if they followed the labsheet), or commercial sets of Soma cubes. You may want to keep the puzzles in an activity area or learning center where small groups of students can take turns trying to find a solution. (The commercial Soma sets have puzzle books that show other constructions students can make with the same seven pieces.) Encourage students to create new puzzle shapes of their own that use some or all of the pieces. Students could, for example, try to build other rectangular prisms.

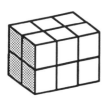 

Sequencing

Encourage students to create sequences of the six arrangements of four cubes according to this rule:

Move one cube one cube's distance.

Example Sequence:

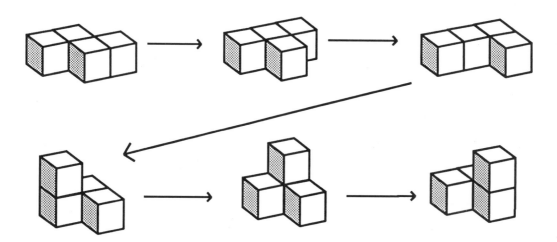

Giant Soma puzzle

Ask each student to bring in six 1-foot squares of cardboard from home. Help students assemble the squares into cubes using masking tape and glue. Then have students combine the cubes to make giant Soma pieces. Cover each piece with papier-mâché and use the giant pieces to make large sculpture solutions.

Independent Exploration   ▢ ▢ ▢ ▢

Once students are familiar with the concept of regular and irregular arrangements of cubes, they may be able to work on this activity independently by following the procedures outlined on Labsheet 23. Each student will need:

> a copy of Labsheet 23
>
> about thirty sugar cubes
>
> white glue
>
> waxed paper

You may want to have students work in small groups so that they can evaluate each other's arrangements. Encourage students to explore several arrangements before gluing them together. If necessary, remind students not to use too much glue and to let the arrangements dry without handling them for at least thirty minutes. (Even then they won't be completely dry, but by the next day they will be solid.) Be sure each group comes up with a complete set of six solutions. Then invite students to come back together as a class to discuss the Soma puzzle and sequences of the six arrangements.

Exploring Arrangements of Four Cubes

Need: Sugar cubes, white glue, waxed paper

24. Exploring Surface Area

☐ ☐ ☐ ☐

Students will find patterns of squares that cover (like a "jacket") the irregular arrangements of four cubes. They will then use the patterns to find the surface area of the arrangements.

Teacher Materials: One 1-inch wooden cube

This hexomino cut out of 1-inch grid paper

Copies of the Soma pieces on page 142

Student Materials: One irregular arrangement of four 1-inch cubes

Several sheets of 1-inch grid paper

Scissors and tape

Getting Started

Fold the cutout of the hexomino into a cube. Then flatten it out again. Hold up the wooden cube and point out to students that it has six faces. Since each of the faces on the 1-inch cube is a square inch, it would take six square inches of paper to cover it. Then ask:

> *Which could be used to cover a cube, a pentomino or a hexomino? (a hexomino)*

Explain to students that a hexomino made of 1-inch squares has the same area as the *surface area* of the 1-inch cube. Show that this is true by placing the cube in the middle of the hexomino cross and folding the hexomino so that it completely covers the cube. Hold up the covered cube and announce:

> *Some people call this hexomino a "jacket" for the cube because it completely covers it.*

Exploring the Problem

Have students use the 1-inch grid paper to make jackets for their irregular arrangements of four cubes.

There are two ways to approach the solution to this problem. Some students may choose to cut out pieces and build a jacket by taping pieces together, testing the jacket, and making modifications as they go. Other students may prefer to draw the whole jacket on the grid paper and cut it out as one piece before testing it. Either way is valid.

Students' choice of method reveals something about their learning style. Students who use the first method tend to be more inductive, starting with the details and working up to the whole. Students who use the second method are usually more deductive, starting with a general overview and working back to the details. Another example of this difference is in students' approach to spelling. Deductive students become familiar with the general configurations of words and would see the word *bag* like drawing (1). Inductive students are aware of the sequence of individual letters and would see the same word like drawing (2).

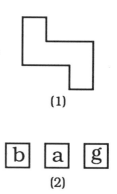

As students continue to work on their jackets, remind them that it is not bad to make mistakes. Some students will want to throw away a jacket that does not fit, but encourage them to study it, modify it, and try again. When all students have completed one jacket, encourage them to compare their jackets with each other. If there is time, some students may want to explore making a jacket for a different arrangement.

Follow-up

Jackets

Post many jackets on the bulletin board and encourage students to examine them. Ask students to identify any jackets that they think are incorrect. Then invite them to remove the jackets from the board and test them. Also encourage students to see if they can determine which arrangement someone was working with by just looking at the flattened jacket. After students have ventured their opinions, have them find out if they are right by trying to cover the arrangements they guessed with the appropriate jackets.

Then have students sort the posted jackets into six groups according to which of the arrangements of four cubes they cover. Repost the sorted groups of jackets on the bulletin board. Use copies of the Soma pieces shown on page 142 to create headings for the groups.

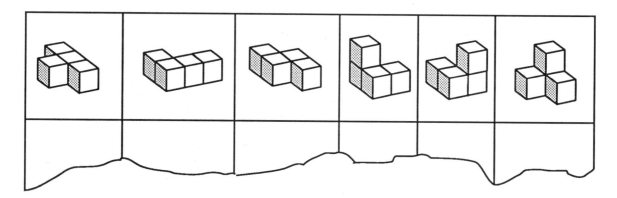

Students will probably have found several different ways to make a jacket for the same arrangement.

Ask students to explain why an arrangement can have more than one jacket. Remind them that in Exploration 22 they found eleven hexomino patterns that could be made into a cube. There are usually several ways that a surface area can be divided up to form a two-dimensional pattern.

104

Surface Area

Ask students to find the surface area of any of the arrangements of four cubes that they have made jackets for. If necessary, point out that they can find the surface area of an arrangement by just counting the squares in its jacket. Students will discover that all six of the irregular arrangements of four cubes have the same surface area: 18 square inches.

Then show students this *regular* arrangement of four cubes and ask them to determine its surface area (16 square inches).

One way to have students find the surface area is to have them construct the square prism out of four 1-inch cubes and then use 1-inch grid paper to make a jacket for it. Students can count the number of squares in the jacket to discover that the surface area is 16 square inches.

Ask students why the surface area of the regular arrangement is different from the surface area of the irregular arrangements. Lead them to observe that all the irregular arrangements have three places where faces of the cubes are hidden. Since the regular arrangement shown has four such places, it has fewer faces exposed.

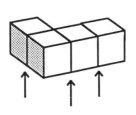 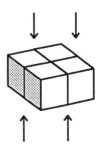

Independent Exploration

If you want to have students work more independently, distribute copies of Labsheet 24. Remind students to read and follow the instructions carefully. Students should work in small groups so that they can compare their jackets with others. When all groups have made several jackets, invite students to come back together as a class to discuss the different arrangements for the same jackets and the surface area of all the arrangements.

Exploring Surface Area

Need: One irregular arrangement of four 1-inch cubes, several sheets of 1-inch grid paper, scissors, tape

25. Exploring Irregular Arrangements of Five Cubes

◻ ◻ ◻ ◻ ◻

Students will experiment to find all the possible irregular arrangements of five cubes.

Student Materials: Five 1-inch cubes
                    Masking tape

Getting Started

Remind students of the irregular arrangements of cubes that they discussed as part of Exploration 23. Then copy this chart onto the chalkboard and have students help you fill it in. (2—0; 3—1; 4—6)

Encourage students to study the chart and predict how many irregular arrangements of five cubes there are.

Number of Cubes	Number of Irregular Arrangements
2	
3	
4	
5	?

Exploring the Problem

Encourage students to arrange their five cubes in as many ways as they can. Allow an appropriate amount of time for students to explore several arrangements. Then ask students to make a model of one of their arrangements by taping five cubes together. Remind them to use small pieces of tape. Neatness counts!

Invite students to bring their taped arrangements to the front of the room. (Or, if you feel the need to have students remain seated, collect the arrangements yourself.) Display the collected arrangements where students can see them. Then have students evaluate each arrangement by determining whether it has five cubes, is irregular, and has shared faces that match up exactly.

Follow-up

Ask students to evaluate the arrangements to see how many different irregular arrangements of five cubes they have found. Before taking out an arrangement that seems to be a duplicate, be sure to have students test it carefully by turning it and comparing it with the other arrangements. Some arrangements that seem to be duplicates may actually be mirror images (see Exploration 23). When students do encounter duplicates, keep the one that is neater and stronger.

After students have eliminated all the duplicates, ask them if any solutions are missing. Give an additional five cubes to any students who think they can come up with a new arrangement. Be sure to have students compare the new arrangements to the ones already in the solution set to verify that they are truly new.

It may help students find missing arrangements that are mirror images of each other if they sort the models into two groups: Mirror and Nonmirror. (See page 113 for the sorting solution.) After students have sorted all the arrangements they have into the two groups, ask:

How are the arrangements in each group alike?

Example responses:

Mirror   All of the arrangements are asymmetrical and have at least two cubes in a stack.

Nonmirror   Most of the arrangements can lie flat and be only one cube in height. Or, if they have two cubes in a stack, the whole arrangement is symmetrical. Some students might point out that the flat arrangements are like three-dimensional pentominoes.

If students point out the three-dimensional pentominoes, ask which one of the twelve pentominoes is missing from this collection (1). Then ask students to tell why it is not part of the collection. If necessary, point out that the missing pentomino is a regular arrangement and that the collection they are working with has only irregular arrangements.

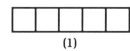

(1)

Have students pair up the mirror images in the Mirror group and construct any arrangements that are missing. All the arrangements are shown on page 113. When all of the solutions have been found, announce:

> There are twenty-eight and only twenty-eight irregular arrangements of five cubes.

Call students' attention to the chart they filled in before starting this exploration. Complete the chart with the number of irregular arrangements of five cubes and ask students to compare the result with any predictions they made earlier.

Independent Exploration

Students can explore arrangements independently by following the procedures outlined on Labsheet 25. Be sure they understand how to record arrangements on the isometric grid paper before turning them loose to discover arrangements. After students have recorded several arrangements, have each student make a model of one of the arrangements. Then use the models in a class discussion in which you evaluate, sort, and complete the solution set.

Exploring Irregular Arrangements of Five Cubes

Need: Five 1-inch cubes

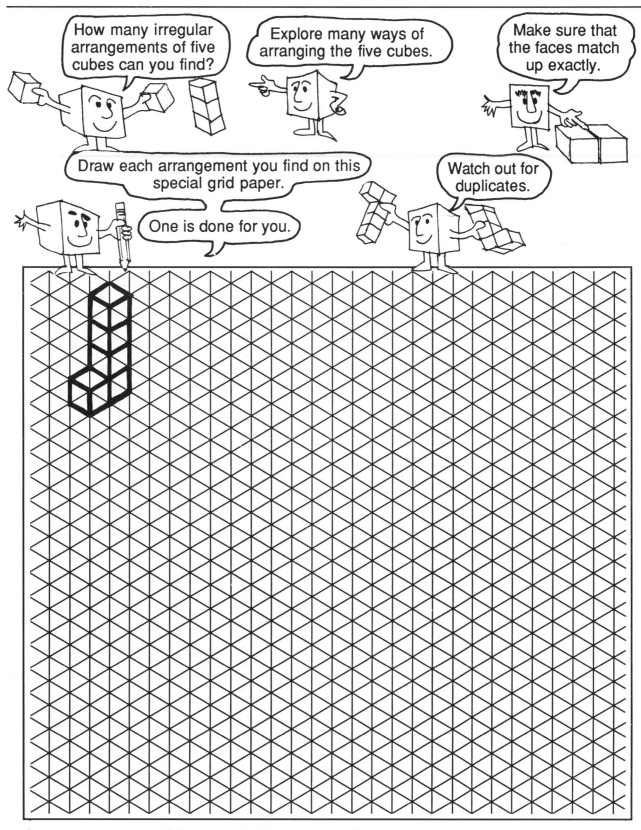

Compare your solutions with those of other students.

26. Constructing 4 × 4 × 4 Cubes

□ □ □ □ □

Students will experiment to find different ways of using twelve arrangements of five cubes and one arrangement of four cubes to build a 4 × 4 × 4 cube.

Note on Materials: Creating sets of all the irregular arrangements for each student would be very time consuming. You may want to create one puzzle center where small groups of students can take turns working. Alternatively, you could have students help you create several puzzle centers so that the groups can work simultaneously. Collect the materials listed below for each puzzle center you want to make.

Student Materials: Set of all the irregular arrangements of three, four, and five cubes

A container for all the arrangements

Several copies of the drawings of these arrangements (pages 112 and 113)

Several 5" × 8" plain index cards

Scissors and paste

Several copies of Labsheet 26

Getting Started

Ask:

Is it possible to build a 4 × 4 × 4 cube with the irregular arrangements of five cubes?

Some students will probably point out that 4 × 4 × 4 = 64, which is not a multiple of 5. Then have students suppose that they will be able to use one Soma piece to build the cube. Ask:

How many arrangements of five cubes would you need in addition to the one arrangement of four cubes?
(64 − 4 = 60; 60 ÷ 5 = 12)

Then ask:

How many different ways can you build a 4 × 4 × 4 cube?

Post this question in the puzzle centers.

110

Exploring the Problem

Allow small groups of students to work at one of the puzzle centers to discover different ways of building $4 \times 4 \times 4$ cubes. Check to be sure that all the students in each group have an opportunity to participate in solving the problem.

After students have found a solution, have them make a record of the arrangements they used by cutting them out of the sheets of drawings and pasting them on an index card. (See the sample puzzle cards on page 115.) Allow students also to create $4 \times 4 \times 4$ cubes using other combinations of arrangements. Some students, for example, may suggest using all six irregular arrangements of four cubes and only eight of the irregular arrangements of five cubes. $[(6 \times 4) + (8 \times 5) = 64]$. Other students might suggest using one arrangement of three cubes, four arrangements of four cubes, and nine arrangements of five cubes $[(9 \times 5) + (4 \times 4) + 3 = 64]$.

Follow-up

Encourage each group to look at a card created by another group and try to build a $4 \times 4 \times 4$ cube with the same arrangements shown on the card. Students will find that although these cubes are fairly easy to construct, it is more difficult to reconstruct a solution from a given set of arrangements.

Collect all the cards and put them in the puzzle centers so that students can try to solve the cubes as they have time.

Independent Exploration　　　　□ □ □ □ □

Keep copies of Labsheet 26 in the puzzle centers so that students can refer to it as they work through this activity. Remind students to read and follow the instructions carefully.

Extension

Present students with the challenge of using the arrangements of five cubes to create an even larger cube. Ask:

> *What is the largest possible cube you can make with the twenty-eight arrangements of five cubes?*

Students will first need to determine how many cubes were used to build the twenty-eight arrangements ($28 \times 5 = 140$). Then they can find the largest cubic number that is a multiple of 5 and is less than 140.

$$1 \times 1 \times 1 = 1 \qquad 4 \times 4 \times 4 = 64$$

$$2 \times 2 \times 2 = 8 \qquad 5 \times 5 \times 5 = 125$$

$$3 \times 3 \times 3 = 27 \qquad 6 \times 6 \times 6 = 216$$

Ask students how many arrangements they would need to build a cube with a volume of 125 cubic units ($125 \div 5 = 25$). There would be three arrangements left over.

Encourage students to try to build the $5 \times 5 \times 5$ cube as they have time available. This is a very difficult puzzle. The solution is given on page 116.

The Only Irregular Arrangement of Three Cubes

The Six Irregular Arrangements of Four Cubes

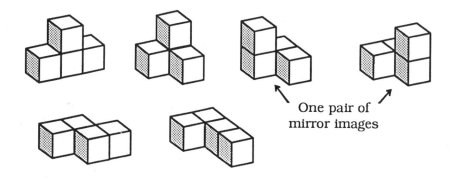

One pair of
mirror images

The Twenty–eight Irregular Arrangements of Five Cubes

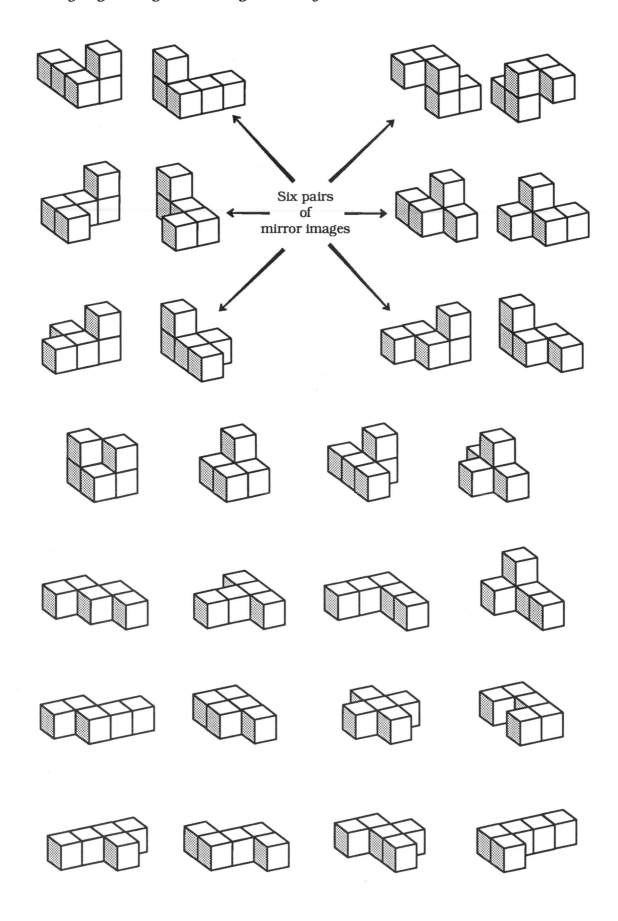

Six pairs
of
mirror images

Constructing 4 x 4 x 4 Cubes

Need: A set of irregular arrangements for three, four, and five cubes; copies of the drawings of the irregular arrangements; several 5" x 8" plain index cards; scissors; paste

Example Solution Cards for the 4 x 4 x 4 Cube

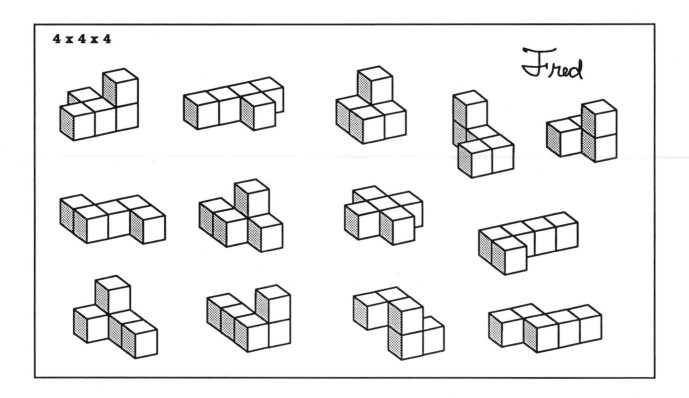

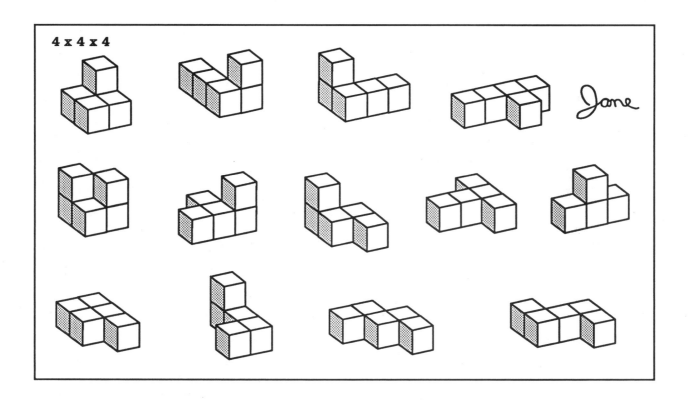

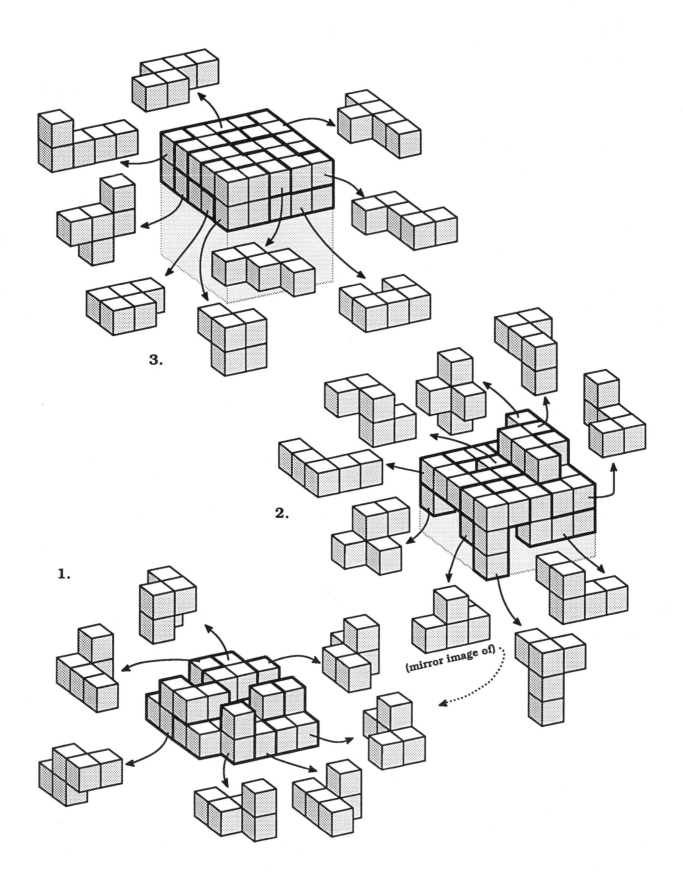

3.

2.

1.

(mirror image of)

27. Constructing 3 × 3 × 3 Cubes   □□□□□

Students will experiment to find different ways of building 3 × 3 × 3 cubes out of the irregular arrangements of three, four, and five cubes.

Student Materials: Students will continue to work at the puzzle center created for Exploration 26. For this activity, add copies of Labsheet 27.

Getting Started

Encourage students to continue working on the problem of building the 5 × 5 × 5 cube. Construct one yourself by following the solution on page 116. Show the completed cube to students so that they will know it is possible. Then start to take it apart so that students can get clues as to how to start building it.

Then have students show the class several of the puzzle cards that they created for 4 × 4 × 4 cubes in Exploration 26. Ask:

Is it possible to use arrangements of five cubes to build 3 × 3 × 3 cubes?

Students should point out that 3 × 3 × 3 = 27, which is not a multiple of 5. Encourage students to consider the possibility of using other irregular arrangements in addition to the arrangements of five cubes. Examples:

- If five arrangements of five cubes were used, two more cubes would be needed (27 ÷ 5 = 5, with remainder 2), but there are no irregular arrangements of two cubes.

- If four arrangements of five cubes were used, seven more cubes would be needed (27 − (4 x 5) = 7). One possibility would be to use one arrangement of four cubes and the one arrangement of three cubes.

- If three arrangements of five cubes were used, twelve more cubes would be needed (27 − (3 x 5) = 12), which could be provided by three arrangements of four cubes.

Then ask:

How many different ways can you build a 3 × 3 × 3 cube?

Post this question in the puzzle centers.

Exploring the Problem

Provide an opportunity for students to work with a group at one of the puzzle centers. Remind students that when working in groups all members of the group should be involved in solving the problem. After a group has created a puzzle card with a solution, encourage them to have someone in the group double-check to be sure the correct arrangements are shown. (Example puzzle cards are shown on page 120.)

Follow-up

Encourage groups to look at one of the cards from another group and try to build a cube with the arrangements shown. Keep all the cards in the puzzle center or centers so that individuals or groups can work on them as they have time available.

Remind students that they have now worked with three different-sized cubes: $5 \times 5 \times 5$, $4 \times 4 \times 4$, and $3 \times 3 \times 3$. Then ask:

Is it possible to construct a $2 \times 2 \times 2$ cube with these irregular arrangements?

Give students a few moments to determine that $2 \times 2 \times 2 = 8$. Then have them think about what combinations of irregular arrangements could have a total of eight cubes. Possible responses:

- Two arrangements of four cubes.
- The one arrangement of three cubes and one arrangement of five cubes.

Invite students to try to build a cube with each of these combinations. Students will find that it is impossible to build a $2 \times 2 \times 2$ cube with two arrangements of four cubes because that would require two identical arrangements, and there is only one arrangement of each type in the solution set. They will, however, find that it is possible to construct the $2 \times 2 \times 2$ cube using one irregular arrangement of five cubes and the only irregular arrangement of three cubes.

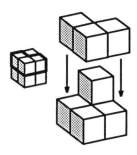

Independent Exploration

Keep copies of Labsheet 27 in the puzzle centers so that students can refer to it as they work through this activity. Remind students to read and follow the instructions carefully. Then have students discuss the possibility of building a $2 \times 2 \times 2$ cube.

Constructing 3 x 3 x 3 Cubes

Need: A set of irregular arrangements for three, four, and five cubes; copies of the drawings of the irregular arrangements; several 5" x 8" plain index cards; scissors; paste

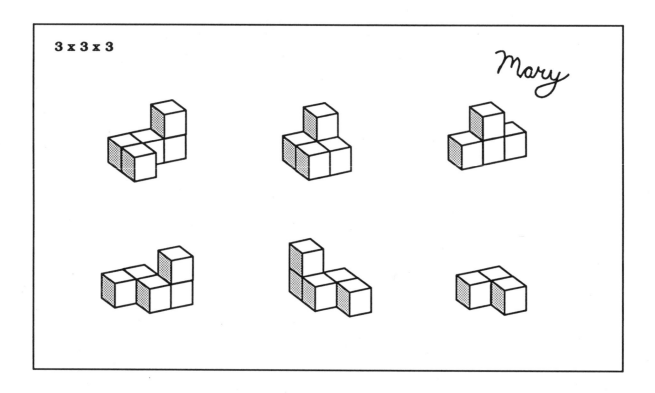

28. Constructing Prisms with Irregular Arrangements of Five Cubes

□ □ □ □ □

Students will experiment to find several different prisms that they can construct with irregular arrangements of five cubes.

Note on Materials: Students will continue to work at the puzzle centers used for Explorations 26 and 27. For this activity, stock the centers with the items listed under "Student Materials."

Teacher Materials: Three or four boxes to serve as examples of prisms (examples: graham cracker, toothpaste, and cake mix boxes)

                         An example of a cube (a cubical box or a cube constructed from the arrangements used in class)

Student Materials: A complete set of the twenty-eight irregular arrangements of five cubes

                         A container for these arrangements

                         Several copies of the drawings of these arrangements (page 113)

                         Several sheets of isometric grid paper (pages 153 or 154)

                         Several sheets of white construction paper, some cut in half

                         Scissors and paste

                         Several copies of Labsheet 28

Getting Started

Hold up the cube so that students can see it. Point out that it is a cube because all of the dimensions are the same. Then show students the other boxes you have collected. Explain to the class that these boxes are rectangular prisms. Have students measure the boxes and list the dimensions on the chalkboard. Examples:

Toothpaste	$1\frac{1}{2} \times 1\frac{1}{2} \times 7$ inches
Cake mix	$5\frac{1}{2} \times 7 \times 1\frac{1}{2}$ inches
Graham crackers	$5\frac{1}{2} \times 8 \times 2\frac{3}{4}$ inches

Ask students to tell how the rectangular prisms are different from the cube. Students should note that unlike a cube, the dimensions of a rectangular prism are not all the same. At least one dimension is different from the other two.

Then challenge students to construct several rectangular prisms. Ask:

How many different prisms can you build using the irregular arrangements of five cubes?

Post this question in the puzzle centers.

Exploring the Problem

Have students work in small groups at the puzzle centers. Provide plenty of time for each group to explore several ways of constructing rectangular prisms. Check to be sure all students have the opportunity to participate. Then instruct students to record each arrangement two ways: by cutting out drawings of the arrangements of five cubes they have used and by drawing a picture that shows the dimensions of the prism on the isometric grid paper. (You may need to demonstrate how to draw the prisms on this kind of grid paper.) Students should then cut out the drawing from the grid paper, leaving a narrow border, and paste this drawing and the cutouts of the various arrangements on a sheet of the white construction paper. (See the sample puzzle cards on page 124.) Encourage students to double-check to be sure that they have pasted down all the correct drawings.

Follow-up

Have each group look at a puzzle sheet from another group and try to recreate the prism shown. Keep all the puzzle sheets in the puzzle centers so that students can work on them as they have time. If two or more puzzle sheets show prisms with the same dimensions, have students compare the arrangements that appear on the sheets. Encourage students also to determine if there are any arrangements that are found in all prisms of certain dimensions.

Independent Exploration   ☐ ☐ ☐ ☐ ☐

Keep copies of Labsheet 28 in the puzzle centers so that students can refer to it as they work through this activity. Remind students to read and follow the instructions carefully. Then have students work on each other's puzzles and compare the arrangements used.

Constructing Prisms with Irregular Arrangements of Five Cubes

Need: A set of 28 irregular arrangements of five cubes, copies of the drawings of the 28 arrangements, a sheet of isometric grid paper, white construction paper, scissors, paste

Example Solution Cards for Prisms

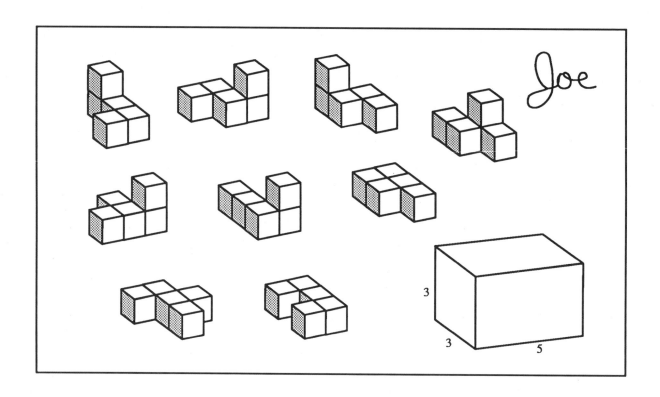

29. Designing Prisms Made of Irregular Arrangements of Five Cubes

□ □ □ □ □

This activity is the inverse of Exploration 28. In this exploration students will first compute the dimensions of a prism and then try to prove that it is possible to build that prism with irregular arrangements of five cubes.

Teacher Materials: Several of the prisms that students discovered in Exploration 28 (either demonstration models made out of the arrangements of five cubes or copies of the puzzle sheets created by the students)

About seventy 4" × 18" strips of manila paper

An example prism container with dimensions 4" × 5" × 3"

Student Materials: Dark crayon

Several sheets of 1-inch grid paper printed on a light colored construction paper

Scissors and tape

Puzzle centers stocked with the following:

   A set of the twenty-eight irregular arrangements of five cubes

   A container for these arrangements

   Several copies of the drawings of these arrangements (page 113)

   Several sheets of white construction paper

   Several sheets of isometric grid paper

   Scissors and paste

   Several copies of Labsheet 29

Getting Started

Show students several of the prisms that were constructed as part of Exploration 28. Then ask:

> *How many prisms are there that have a volume that is a multiple of 5 and is less than or equal to 140 cubic units?*

Pass out several strips of the manila paper to each student. Have students use a dark crayon to write the dimensions of prisms that would satisfy these conditions. Instruct them to write the dimensions of each prism on a separate strip.

Collect the strips and post them on the bulletin board. Help students evaluate each of the equations by asking the questions on the next page.

$$4 \times 5 \times 5 = 100$$

$$4 \times 4 \times 5 = 80$$

$$1 \times 6 \times 10 = 60$$

- *Is the volume of the prism less than or equal to 140 cubic units?*
- *Is the volume a multiple of 5?*

If the answer to either question is "no," remove the equation from the board.

Exploring the Problem

There are two steps to this exploration. In step 1 students will use the 1-inch grid paper and tape to construct prisms without tops. Then in step 2 students will test these prisms to see if they can be filled with the irregular arrangements of five cubes.

Have students use the 1-inch grid paper to build several prisms without tops. Show them the example container that you built before class. Caution students to cut the grid paper accurately and to tape the containers neatly and securely. As students complete their containers, ask them to contribute them to a class collection in the front of the room. Encourage students to evaluate each of the containers in the collection and remove any that do not have volumes that are multiples of 5 and are less than or equal to 140 cubic units. Then have students study the collection and determine if any are missing.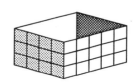

Post this question in the puzzle centers:

Which prisms can you fill with irregular arrangements of five cubes?

Have students form small groups and distribute the containers among them. Then provide an opportunity for each group to work at a puzzle center where they will try to fill the containers with the irregular arrangements of five cubes. Instruct students to record their solutions by cutting out and pasting down drawings of the irregular arrangements they have used. Also have students draw the dimensions of the prisms on isometric grid paper, cut the drawings out, and paste them on the same paper.

Students will find some containers that are impossible to solve with the given arrangements. Remove those containers from the collection and put them in a separate place. Some students will, of course, try to find a solution for these prisms just because someone else has declared them impossible to solve.

Follow-up

Encourage students to examine the collection of prisms without solutions. Ask:

Why is it impossible to fill some of the containers with the irregular arrangements of five cubes?

Example responses:

There is no *irregular* arrangement of five cubes that would fit into this regular prism with a volume of 5 cubic units.

Two arrangements of five cubes could fit into this prism only if they were identical.

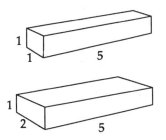

There aren't enough arrangements of five cubes that are only 1 inch high. ($6 \times 1 \times 10 = 60$, and $60 \div 5 = 12$, but there are only eleven arrangements that are only 1 inch high.)

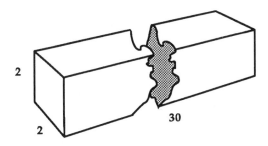

There aren't enough arrangements that are 2 inches wide. ($2 \times 2 \times 30 = 120$, and $120 \div 5 = 24$, but there are only twenty-two arrangements that are 2 inches wide.)

If students have not yet discovered a prism that has a volume of 140 cubic units, challenge them to build the prism with dimensions $5 \times 4 \times 7$. This is a difficult puzzle to solve. See page 129 for the solution. Some students may have suggested other dimensions for prisms that have a volume of 140 cubic units. Encourage students to try to use all the arrangements to build those prisms as well.

Independent Exploration

Keep copies of Labsheet 29 in the puzzle centers so that students can refer to it as they work through this activity. Remind students to read and follow the instructions carefully. When all groups have explored several prisms, invite students to come back together as a class to discuss why some of the prisms are impossible to solve.

Designing Prisms Made of Irregular Arrangements of Five Cubes

Step 1 | Need: 1-inch grid paper, scissors, tape

Step 2 | Need: A set of all 28 irregular arrangements of five cubes, copies of the drawings of the arrangements, isometric grid paper, white construction paper, scissors, paste

128

Whole Set Solution for All Twenty–eight Pieces
(4 x 5 x 7 Prism)

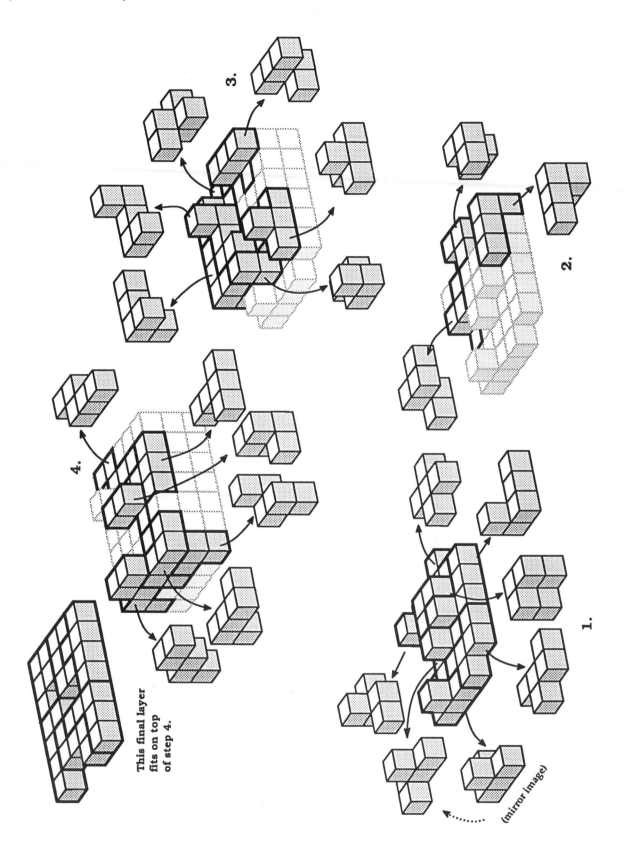

1.

2.

3.

4.

(mirror image)

This final layer fits on top of step 4.

30. Constructing Symmetrical Solids with Irregular Arrangements of Five Cubes

□ □ □ □ □

Students will solve and create puzzles that involve building symmetrical solids out of the twenty-eight irregular arrangements of five cubes.

Teacher Materials: Models of the irregular arrangements:

Student Materials: Puzzle centers stocked with the following:

A set of the twenty-eight irregular arrangements of five cubes

A container for these arrangements

Copies of the puzzles on page 133

Isometric grid paper

5" × 8" index cards

Scissors and paste

Copies of Labsheet 30

Getting Started

Hold up the models of the two irregular arrangements. Then put them together to demonstrate the construction of a symmetrical solid.

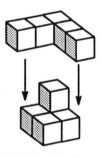 

If necessary, remind students that a figure is symmetrical if you can draw a line through the center of it and have both halves look the same (see Exploration 9). Ask:

> *How could you draw a line on this solid so that it divides the solid into two identical halves?*

Here are two ways:

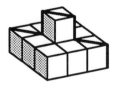 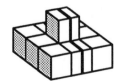

If time allows, have students sort the twenty-eight irregular arrangements of five cubes into two groups: symmetrical and asymmetrical.

Exploring the Problem

Have groups of students work at the puzzle centers to complete the three tasks for this activity. The first task is to use the arrangements of five cubes to solve the puzzles on page 133. Encourage students to keep trying until they find a solution. The solutions are given on page 134.

The second task for students is to invent symmetrical shapes of their own. They can use any number of arrangements to build the shapes, but should double-check the end result to be sure that it is symmetrical.

The third task is to create puzzle cards that other students can solve. Instruct students to make a careful drawing of their symmetrical solid on the isometric grid paper. Then have them cut out the drawing and paste it on an index card. Keep all the puzzle cards in the puzzle centers so that students can select different ones to work on.

Follow-up

Post a number of the puzzle cards on the bulletin board. Ask students to evaluate each one for symmetry. Can it be divided into two identical halves? If students think that some solids look impossible to build, have them check the drawings to be sure they are correct.

Independent Exploration ⬜⬜⬜⬜⬜

Keep copies of Labsheet 30 in the puzzle centers so that students can refer to it as they work through this activity. Remind students to read and follow the instructions carefully. When all groups have made at least one puzzle, post the puzzles on the bulletin board and have students evaluate the solids for symmetry.

Extension

Some students may enjoy constructing asymmetrical solids and naming them. Example:

Dead Dinosaur

Constructing Symmetrical Solids with Irregular Arrangements of Five Cubes

Step 1 Need: A set of the 28 irregular arrangements of five cubes, a copy of the puzzle page

A Use the irregular arrangements of five cubes to construct the symmetrical solids that are shown on the puzzle page.

Be patient! It may take several attempts to find the solution.

B Try to invent a symmetrical shape of your own.

Step 2 Need: Isometric grid paper, a 5" x 8" index card, scissors, paste

After you build a symmetrical shape, make a drawing of it on the grid paper.

Cut out the drawing and paste it on an index card.

Trade cards with someone else. Try to solve each other's puzzle.

EXPLORING WITH SQUARES AND CUBES
© Dale Seymour Publications

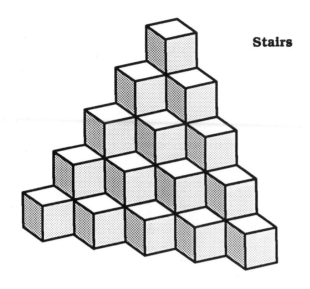

Stairs

Pyramid

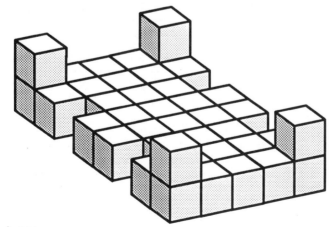

Fortress

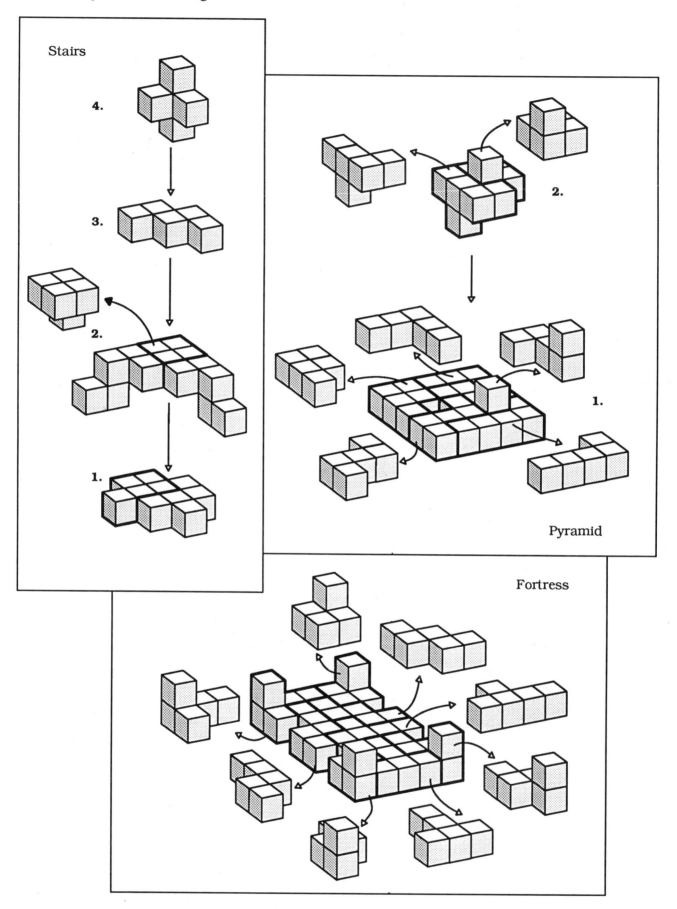

Stairs

4.

3.

2.

1.

2.

1.

Pyramid

Fortress

31. Sorting Irregular Arrangements of Five Cubes □□□□□

Students will sort the irregular arrangements of five cubes according to which irregular arrangements of four cubes are embedded in them.

Teacher Materials: Models of the six irregular arrangements of four cubes

Six shallow boxes or file box lids

A set of the twenty-eight irregular arrangements of five cubes

Getting Started

Line up the six shallow boxes where students can see them. Place one of the arrangements of four cubes by each one.

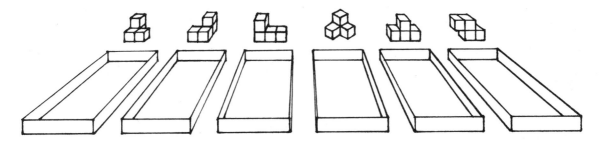

Tell students that every irregular arrangement of five cubes can be made by adding one cube to one of the irregular arrangements of four cubes. Then hold up this arrangement of five cubes and ask:

Which arrangement of four cubes could be used to make this arrangement of five cubes?

Place the arrangement of five cubes in the box in front of one of the arrangements that could be used to make it.

Exploring the Problem

Invite students to take turns choosing an irregular arrangement of five cubes and putting it into one of the boxes according to which arrangement of four cubes is embedded in it. Encourage students to evaluate the accuracy of each placement. If students discover an error, have them move the arrangement to a different box.

Follow-up

If when all the arrangements of five cubes have been sorted there are any boxes that are empty or have just one arrangement in them, ask students to move the arrangements around so that each box has at least four arrangements. Continue to have students evaluate the accuracy of each placement. One possible solution is shown by the shaded arrangements on page 138.

135

32. Exploring Multiple Roots of Irregular Arrangements of Five Cubes □ □ □ □ □

This activity is an extension of Exploration 31. Here students will find all the irregular arrangements of four cubes that could be used to make each irregular arrangement of five cubes.

Teacher Materials: One colored paper cutout of each of the enlarged drawings of irregular arrangements of four and five cubes (see pages 139–142)

Butcher paper

Three white paper cutouts of each of the drawings on pages 139–141

A box for all the white cutouts

Double-sided tape or glue

Getting Started

Copy the chart below onto butcher paper. Paste one of the colored cutouts of the six irregular arrangements of four cubes at the top of each column.

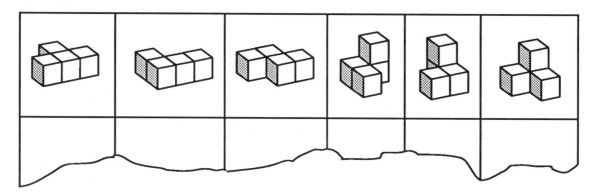

Then paste the colored cutouts of the twenty-eight arrangements of five cubes to show how the arrangements were sorted into boxes in Exploration 31. (You may want to give this job to a group of students who have some extra time.) At this point the chart will look like the shaded portion of the chart shown on page 138. Explain to students that this chart represents the sorting boxes from the previous exploration.

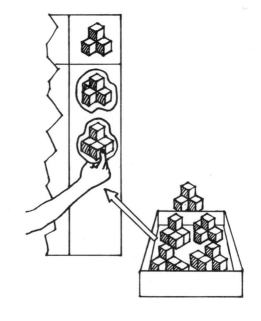

136

Exploring the Problem

Put all the white cutouts of the arrangements into the box from which students will select them.

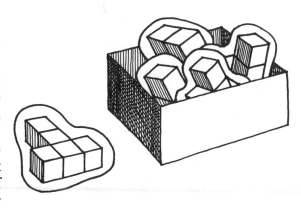

Remind students that in the previous exploration they found that most of the irregular arrangements of five cubes could have been placed in more than one sorting box. Then invite several students to each select an arrangement from the box and post it in an appropriate column of the chart in which it doesn't already appear.

If you are using glue, you may want to have the class evaluate each placement before it is pasted down. (Using double-sided tape makes it easier to move the arrangements around if errors are discovered.)

After awhile the chart will contain the original twenty-eight arrangements plus the duplicates that have just been added by students. Encourage students to find arrangements of five cubes that can be posted in three different columns. Continue having students post the duplicate (and triplicate) arrangements until they are satisfied that the chart is complete. An example chart is given on page 138.

Follow-up

Encourage students to examine the completed chart. After allowing them time to do so, ask them to describe any patterns or characteristics they see.

Example Responses:

1. The least common embedded shape is

2. The most common embedded shape is

3. The following arrangements fit in only one column:

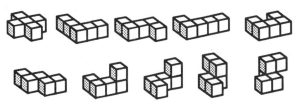

4. The following arrangements fit in three different columns:

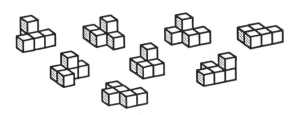

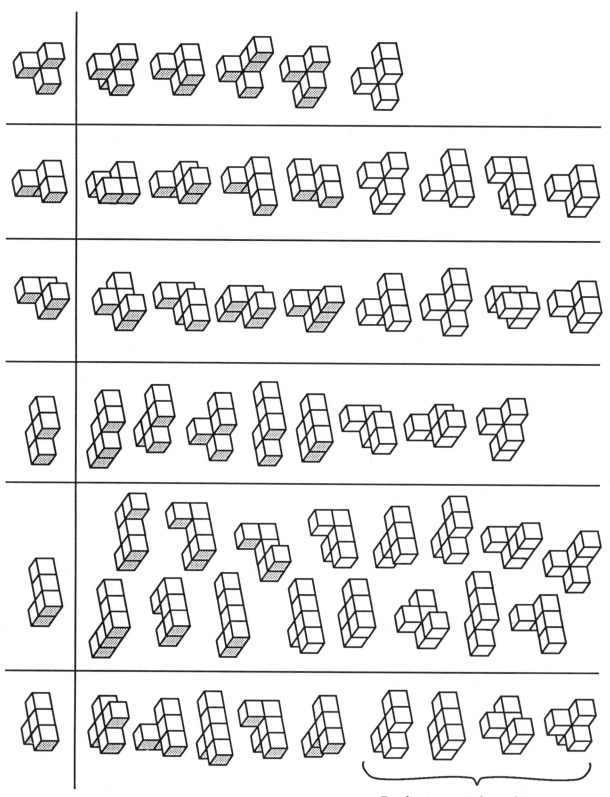

Duplicates copied on white paper

EXPLORING WITH SQUARES AND CUBES
© Dale Seymour Publications

Enlarged Drawings of the Twenty-eight Irregular Arrangements of Five Cubes

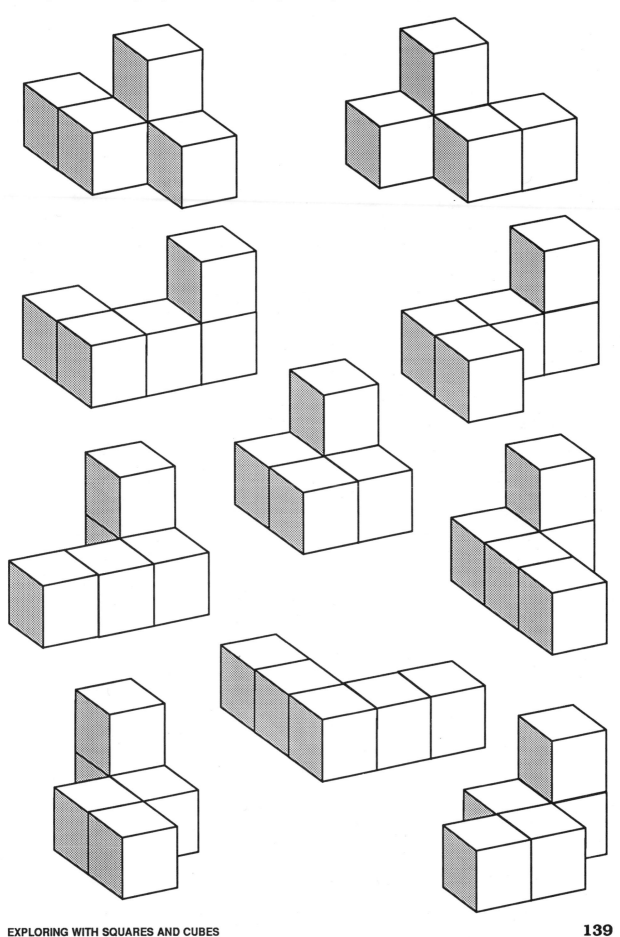

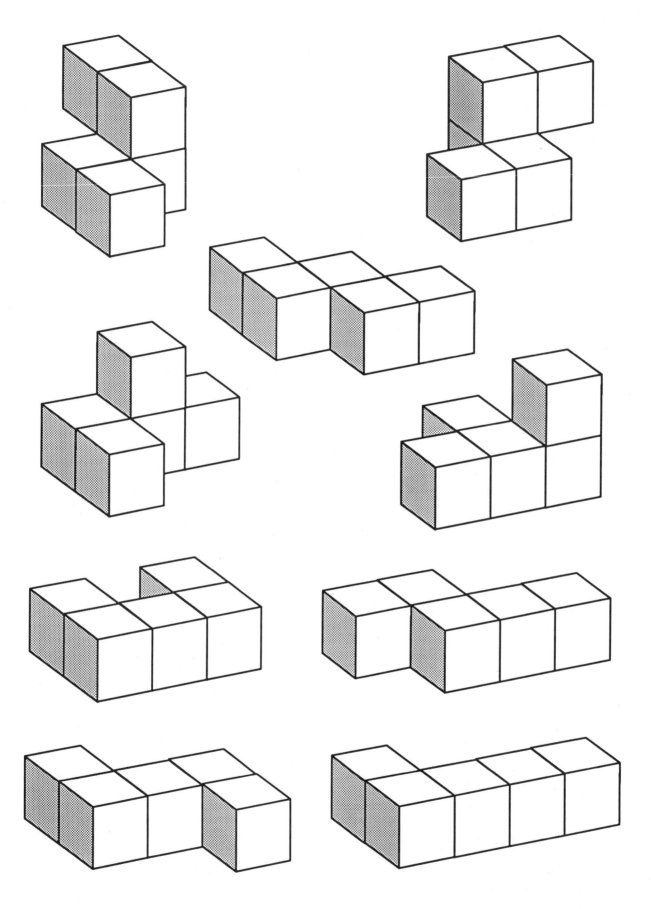

Enlarged Drawings of the Twenty-eight Irregular Arrangements of Five Cubes (continued)

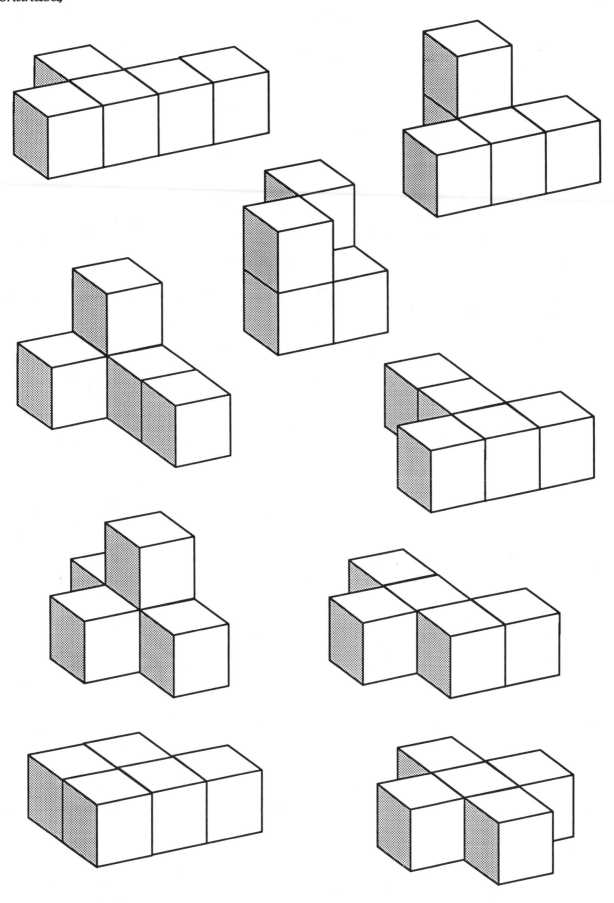

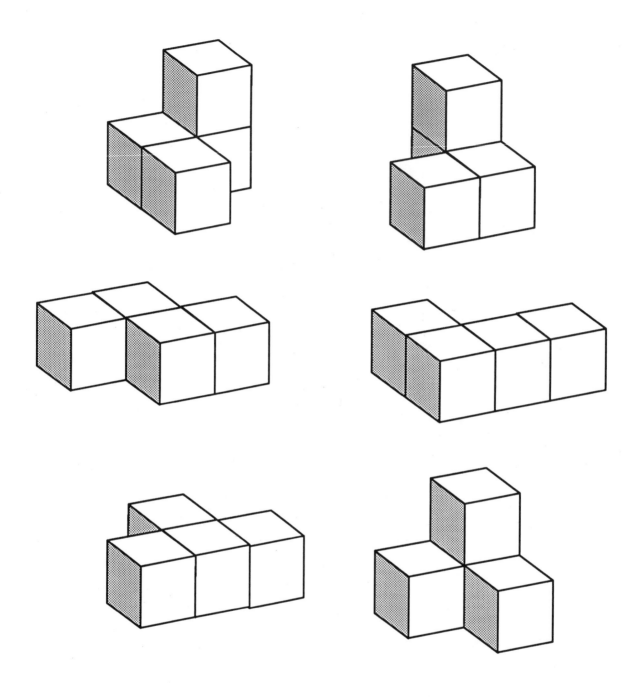

33. Sequencing Irregular Arrangements of Five Cubes

☐ ☐ ☐ ☐ ☐

Students will create sequences of the irregular arrangements of five cubes in which each arrangement can be made by moving one cube in the preceding arrangement one cube's distance.

Teacher Materials: A demonstration model of the arrangement of five cubes

Student Materials: Five 1-inch cubes

Copies of the drawings of the irregular arrangements of five cubes (pages 139–141)

Several 4" × 8" strips of manila paper

Scissors and paste

Getting Started

If you feel that it is necessary to review the concept of sequencing, remind students that sequencing is a way of ordering the members of a set according to a particular rule (see Exploration 10).

Exploring the Problem

Hold up the model of the arrangement of five cubes and have students construct this arrangement with the five cubes on their desks. Then ask:

If you moved one cube one cube's distance, what would the new arrangement look like?

Allow time for students to try some different ways of rearranging the cubes according to this rule. Example arrangements:

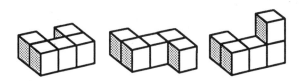

Choose one of the arrangements students have created, make a demonstration model of it, and place it beside the first one. Example:

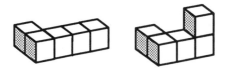

Be sure to put this beginning of the sequence where all students can see it. Have students use the five cubes on their desks to create the second arrangement shown above. Then ask:

If you moved one cube in the second arrangement one cube's distance, what would the new arrangement look like?

Again allow students to experiment making new arrangements according to this rule. Example arrangements:

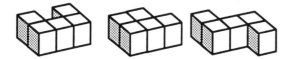

Choose one of their arrangements, create a demonstration model of it, and place it in line with the others. Example sequence:

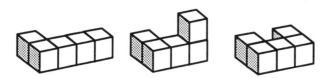

Cut out drawings of the three arrangements (pages 139–141) and paste them in order on one of the 4" × 8" strips. Then draw arrows to demonstrate how to record a sequence.

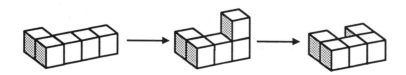

Encourage students to try to build a sequence of their own. Instruct them to build any irregular arrangement of five cubes and then follow the sequencing rule by moving one cube each time to create a new arrangement. Encourage students to cut out the drawing for each arrangement before creating another one. Sometimes students will find several arrangements for a sequence and then forget which ones they were before they cut them out. Other students may remember all their arrangements but cut out three or four at a time and put them in the wrong order. Remind students to make a record of the sequences by pasting down the arrangements and drawing arrows between them.

When students have created sequences of at least five or six arrangements, encourage them to post the arrangements on the bulletin board. While some students will stop at the five or six you have requested, others will try to find very long sequences. If students need additional space to create their sequences, have them tape two or more strips together.

Follow-up

Encourage students to examine the sequences posted on the bulletin board. If students see any strips that could be combined to create a longer sequence, have them connect those sequences together. Then ask:

> Is it possible to put all twenty-eight irregular arrangements of five cubes into just one sequence?

Allow time for students to work on this problem by trying to reorganize the sequences on the board. If there are too many duplicate arrangements in the posted sequences, have students start all over again by cutting out drawings of all twenty-eight arrangements and manipulating them on the board (pinning and repinning). If students cannot find a linear sequence, remind them of the possibility of creating a branching sequence (see Exploration 21).

Note: Now might be a good time to review the behavioral verbs students have discussed earlier (see "Setting the Stage" on page *xii*). Are there any verbs that students want to add to the list now that they have completed all of the activities in this book?

Independent Exploration   ☐ ☐ ☐ ☐ ☐

Some students may be able to work on this activity independently by following the procedures outlined on Labsheet 33. Remind them to read the discussion and the instructions carefully. After individual students have created sequences on their own, have them evaluate each other's sequences according to the sequencing rule and then try to combine them to form a longer one.

Sequencing Irregular Arrangements of Five Cubes

Need: Five 1-inch cubes, copies of the drawings of the irregular arrangements of five cubes, several 4" x 18" strips of manila paper, scissors, paste

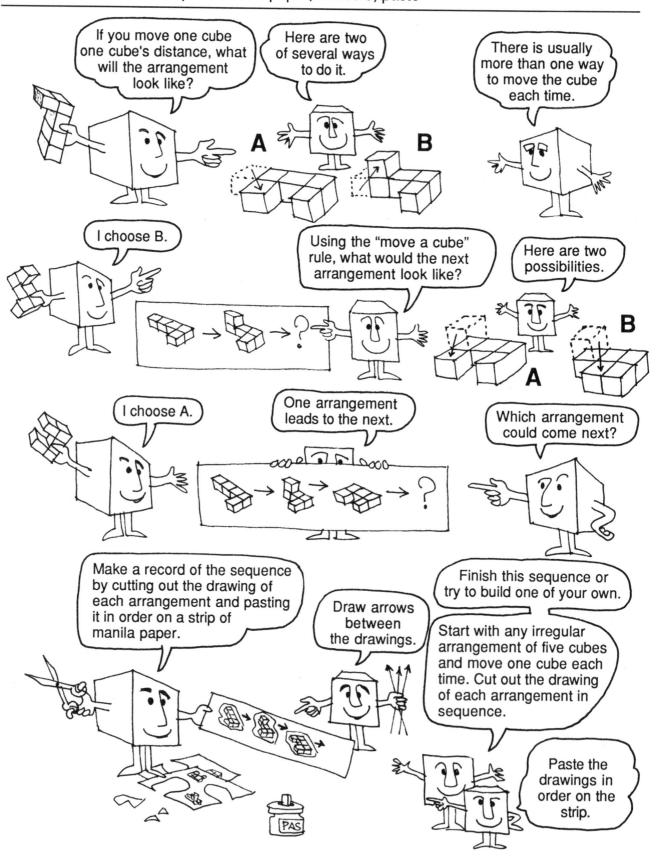

Grid Paper Patterns

□ □ □ □ □ □ □ □ □ □

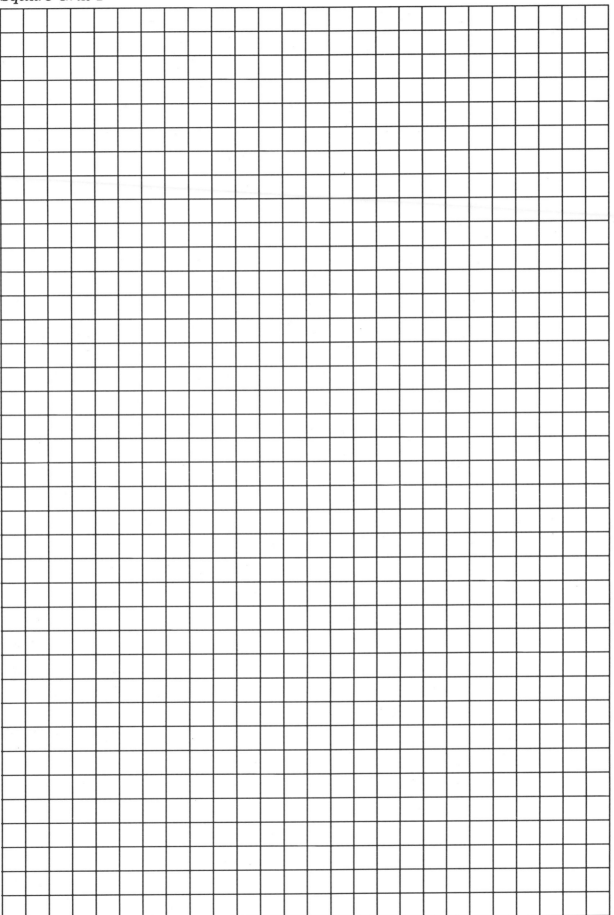

Square Grid 3

Square Grid 4

EXPLORING WITH SQUARES AND CUBES
© Dale Seymour Publications

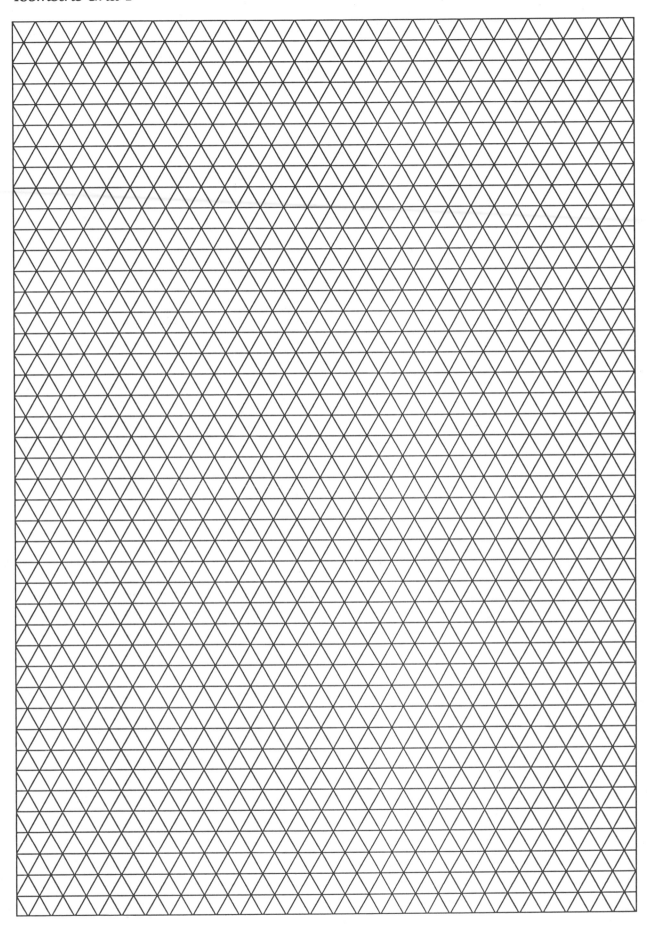